The World of the Bat

LIVING WORLD BOOKS   John K. Terres, Editor

The World of the
Bat

by Charles E. Mohr

J. B. Lippincott Company
Philadelphia and New York

Frontispiece photograph by H. E. Edgerton
from National Audubon Society

U.S. Library of Congress Cataloging in Publication Data

Mohr, Charles E.
The world of the bat.

(Living world books)
Bibliography: p.
Includes index.
1. Bats. I. Title.
QL737.C5M7   599'.4   76–7355
ISBN–0–397–00800–7

Contents

Introduction

MY LIFELONG PREOCCUPATION with bats, which sprang from the chance discovery of a rare species, has led to a stimulating, informative association with scores of scientists. The role many of them have played in transforming the image of the bat from that of a loathsome creature to that of a fascinating, respected member of natural ecosystems will emerge both from the text and from the impressive list of some of the published reports of these scientists.

Many persons have shared with me their interest in, and concern for, bats and other cave creatures: naturalists and superintendents of Mammoth Cave, Carlsbad Caverns, Jewel Cave, and other units of the National Park Service; of U.S. National Forests in Arkansas, Missouri, and California; and of state parks in Florida, Kentucky, Tennessee, Texas, and elsewhere; as well as owners of commercial and undeveloped caves without number.

For forty years Donald R. Griffin, now of Rockefeller University, has shared experience and given advice which I have deeply appreciated. Alvin Novick of Yale University provided invaluable counsel while reviewing an early version, as did Wayne B. Davis of the University of Kentucky, coauthor of *Bats of America*. The second coauthor, Roger W. Barbour, has contributed very substantially by supplying fourteen of his fine portraits of American bats, with the approval of the University Press of Kentucky. I am grateful to Edward R. Buchler for critically reviewing the manuscript.

At the Bird and Mammal Laboratories, National Museum of Natural History, Clyde Jones, Don E. Wilson, and Arthur M. Greenhall have been particularly helpful. So have John D. Hall of Albright College and Merlin D. Tuttle of the Milwaukee Public Museum, whose field studies of endangered cave bats have laid the groundwork for promising recovery plans. The help of many more scientists, here unnamed, will be recognized through photographs or descriptions of their work. Earl L. Poole directed the scientific surveys at the Reading (Pa.) Public Museum that included and inspired my studies of bats.

Travels in search of bats have taken me to wondrous places, many of them now vigilantly guarded by Federal or state agencies or private owners so that bats and all other wildlife will have greater assurance of an adequate and healthy environment—for their benefit and for ours.

Dover, Delaware   CHARLES E. MOHR
September 1975

The tropical American bulldog bat, Noctilio, *flies strongly on long, wide wings, emits powerful sonar pulses, and with huge claws gaffs any fish that breaks the surface. (H. E. Edgerton from National Audubon Society)*

Meet the Bat

THE BATS MADE no sound as I picked their cold, seemingly lifeless forms from the walls of central Pennsylvania's Woodward Cave. Nothing broke the silence in the dark cavern except an occasional splash of water dripping from stalactites and the ripple of wings as a few bats, aroused by my explorations, banked sharply to avoid me in the dark, narrow cave passages. At that time—it was 1931—it seemed logical to suppose that the bats detected my presence in their path through changes in air pressure on their sensitive wings. As late as 1939 Glover M. Allen, in his classic book *Bats,* repeated this theory; but only months later, at the 1940 meeting of the American Association for the Advancement of Science, Donald R. Griffin, one of Allen's students, electrified his fellow scientists with the news that bats were capable of producing sounds in the ultrasonic range—beyond men's hearing—and of navigating by listening to the echoes. With this announcement Griffin ushered in an era of scientific investigation that has established the bat as a prime research subject.

While Griffin's discovery stimulated fresh interest, fascination with bats was not new. Ancient peoples observed bats closely. Wall paintings in a 4,000-year-old Egyptian tomb picture a fruit bat of a variety still common in Egypt. Two of Aesop's fables relate to bats, and statements about bats by other Greek writers, including Aristotle and Pliny, were widely quoted for centuries. In Guatemala I have seen

13

2,000-year-old carvings of the Mayan bat god, Tzinacan, symbolic of caverns, darkness, and death. In the eighteenth century Lazzaro Spallanzani in Italy and Charles Jurine in Switzerland investigated the bat's mysterious ability to navigate in the dark. They were ridiculed when they credited the faculty to hearing.

The notion that bats use sound to navigate did not find easy acceptance even in our own century. In 1912, for example, few persons took notice when American-born inventor Sir Hiram Maxim suggested that sounds inaudible to human ears might be useful to bats. If depth-sounding vibrations could reveal the presence of unseen, underwater obstacles to navigators on shipboard, he asked, might not bats rely on some unidentified sound pulse that they emitted? Nobody seemed to be interested. How could a bat make a sound that no human being could hear? Again, when an English physiologist, Professor H. Hartridge, suggested in 1920 that bats might emit high-frequency sounds and detect echoes from unseen objects in their flight path, nobody pursued the idea.

Except for these latter investigations, most of the interest in bats over the centuries has not been scientific; and the popular interest has stemmed, for the most part, not from curiosity but from fear.

In Eastern Europe during medieval times, it was believed that disembodied spirits—vampires—rose from the grave to fly by night, attacking people and drinking their blood. Centuries later, when blood-drinking bats were discovered in Tropical America, the image of bats in the Western World was not terribly enhanced. Even small, insect-eating bats were feared and loathed.

The most notable exception to the feeling that bats are repulsive is found in parts of China. There bats have long been highly regarded, even held as sacred. The pronunciation for the Chinese word *fu*, the symbol for happiness and good luck, is the same as for the symbol for bat; and, in Chinese art and handicraft, designs of a stylized bat are frequently used to symbolize happiness. But despite

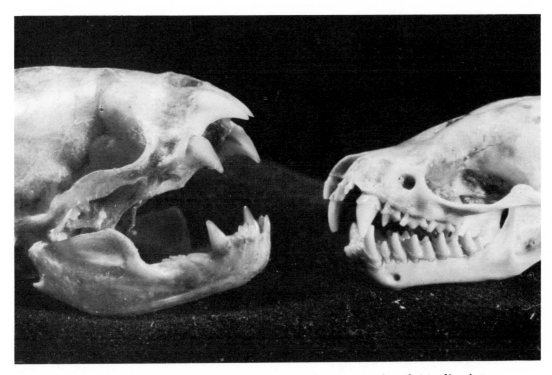

The projecting upper incisor teeth of the vampire bat, Desmodus *(left), slice into skin or hide for bloodletting. The big brown bat,* Eptesicus *(right), chops insects into fine fragments.*

this favorable Oriental opinion, the popular Western view of bats was until recently similar to that of spiders, snakes, and rats: repulsive creatures, to be avoided.

A succession of discoveries about the bat's remarkable nature followed Griffin's echolocation revelations. These have done much to discredit the superstitions that have prejudiced thinking for centuries, but many misconceptions remain.

Classification. A bat is a bat, most people would say. Actually, bats exist in astonishing variety. In the United States alone there are forty different species. Worldwide, at least 847 species are known. Of all the mammals classified by zoologists, one out of seven species is a bat.

15

Only rodents, which include about 350 genera, outrank bats, which have about 175 genera. The order Carnivora is in third place.

Popularly, bats have long been associated with mice, but even the most superficial examination reveals that the bat's teeth, skeleton, and organs are most like those of the insect-eating moles and shrews, included in the mammalian order Insectivora. The scientific classification of bats puts them in the order Chiroptera, a name coined from two Greek words, meaning hand-winged.

Bats are divided into two major groups or suborders, the Megachiroptera or megabats and the Microchiroptera or microbats. All megabats are members of a single family, the Pteropodidae (fruit bats), with numerous species distributed throughout the world from Africa and Asia to Australia. Microbats form a more varied and more successful worldwide group which has exploited a greater range of ecological niches and a wider variety of foods.

Until recently, all that the scientific world knew of the bat's distant ancestors was that batlike flying mammals existed during the Eocene period, fifty million years ago. A few bones from a dozen fossilized skeletons found in Germany had indicated that this creature might have closely resembled modern bats, but the evidence was fragmentary. Then, among thousands of fossil fish entombed in shale beds at the bottom of a shallow lake in Wyoming, a single fossil bat was found. After long study, Princeton's Glenn L. Jepsen reported in 1966 that this uniquely complete specimen differed from the modern-day bats of North America in only one major detail: instead of having a single separate clawed thumb as all our American bats do, *Icaronycteris* had *two* clawed digits separate from the rest of the wing, a characteristic of the megabats. In a sense it is a link between the two bat groups, but Jepsen places it with the microbats.

Megabats such as the flying foxes of Southeast Asia, Australia, and the Southwest Pacific are huge. At the American Museum of Natural History in New York City, my fellow Explorers Club member, Ho-

Bats have changed little since this bat fell into a lake in Wyoming 50 million years ago. It was named Icaronycteris *for Icarus, whose wings of wax and feathers melted when he flew too near the sun;* nycteris *means "of the night."*

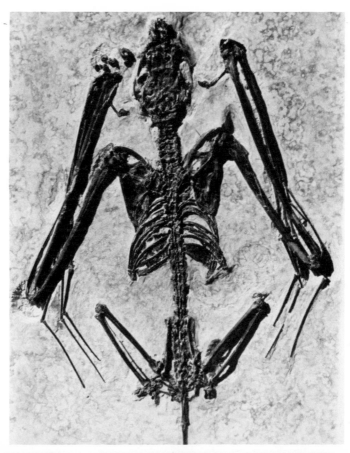

The skeleton of a tropical American fruit bat, Molossus.

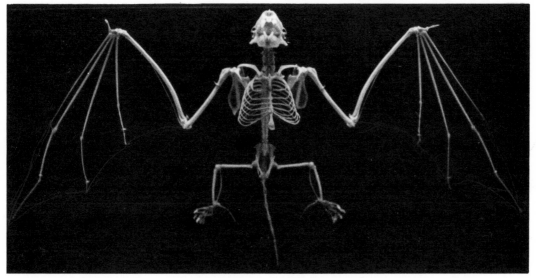

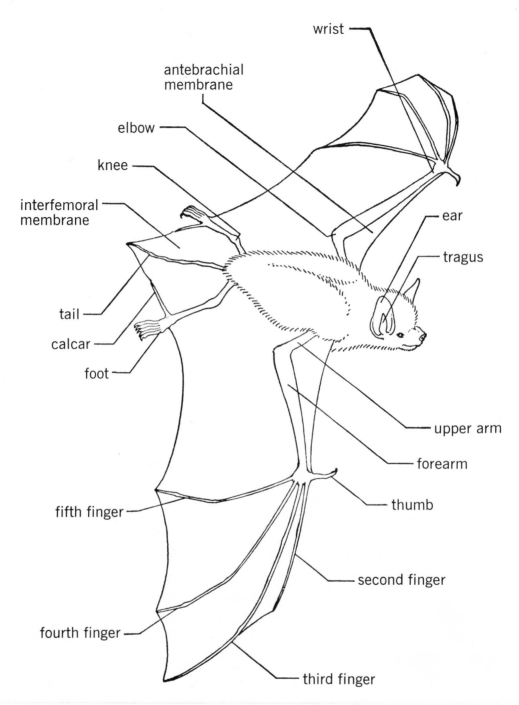

wrist

antebrachial
membrane

elbow

knee

interfemoral
membrane

ear

tragus

tail

calcar

foot

upper arm

forearm

fifth finger

thumb

second finger

fourth finger

third finger

Anatomy of a microbat such as the little brown bat. (The drawing, by Russell Peterson, author of Silently, by Night, *is reproduced courtesy of McGraw-Hill.)*

bart VanDeusen, showed me the world's largest bat, a flying fox, *Pteropus neohibernicus,* which he collected in Papua, New Guinea. He had found its wingspan to be 70 inches—but it weighed only two pounds. There is enough flesh on a flying fox to make it a welcome addition to the native diet, he said. While there are a number of species of flying foxes measuring 4 feet or more in wingspan, some megabats have wingspans of only 12 inches.

Bats Without Sonar. Big megabats have prominent eyes in their dog-like or foxlike faces, so it is no surprise that they depend on vision to reach feeding areas and on the sense of smell to locate ripe fruit. Echolocation is practiced by a single genus of megabats, *Rousettus,* found from Africa to Malaysia, but these bats navigate through dark caves by producing audible clicks with their tongues which resemble the sounds used by the oilbird, *Steatornis,* in Trinidad and Venezuela to navigate inside caves.

As their name implies, microbats are smaller than most megabats. The largest is the tropical American false vampire, *Vampyrum spectrum,* found from southern Mexico to the lower Amazon. It has a wingspan of 32 to 40 inches, and its weight may reach seven ounces. At first, the false vampire was believed to drink blood like a vampire bat, but it is now known to be carnivorous, eating small birds, rodents, and other bats. A number of American zoos display these bats and report them to be tame and gentle toward man, if not toward their victims.

The smallest microbats are truly tiny. The Philippine bamboo bat, *Tylonycteris pachyous,* is generally cited as the smallest bat, and it is possibly the world's smallest mammal. Its forearms may measure as little as 22 mm. Our western American pipistrelle, with a forearm of 27 mm, or the least brown bat, *Myotis leibii,* with a forearm of 28 mm, holds our miniature-size record.

Bats are essentially tropical animals, though a few species of micro-

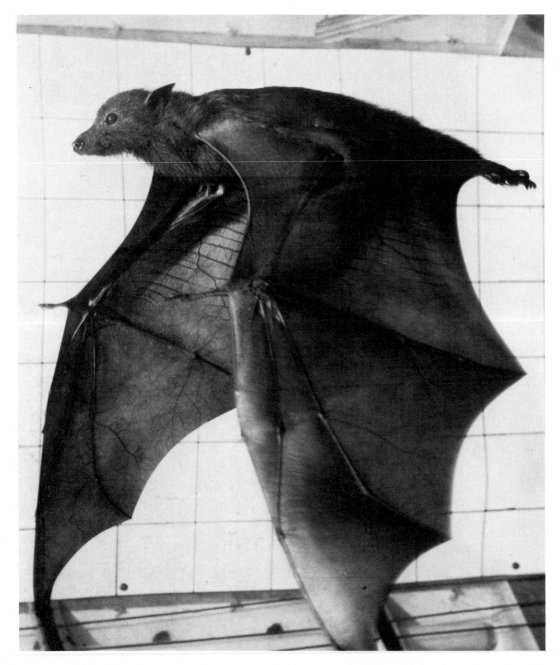

This flying fox, a megabat, can maintain a speed of 16 mph for four hours in this wind tunnel. (Roger E. Carpenter)

bats do reach the edge of the frigid zone, at the limit of trees. There, for a few months, they find enough flying insects to meet their energy needs. In the tropics, however, food is plentiful year round for bats that eat fruit, nectar, and insects as well as for other bats that consume flesh, fish, and the blood of mammals and birds.

Mammals That Fly. The single unique feature of all bats, of course, is their ability to fly. Only three groups of living things can fly: in-

In Australia "camps" of flying foxes may number 2 to 4 million. Vision and smell guide them to their food. (Roger W. Barbour)

sects, birds, and bats. A few kinds of birds have lost the ability to fly, but no species of bat is flightless. While the word "flying" is part of the name of certain other mammals, none of them can fly. The flying squirrel, for example, glides through the air rather than flying. In Southeast Asia, Australia, and the Southwest Pacific there are other so-called "flying" mammals, but no mammal except the bat can really fly.

Most creatures are too heavy to fly. The ancient flying reptiles, pterosaurs (pterodactyls), and the first birds achieved a major breakthrough in weight reduction: they developed hollow bones. In addition, they discarded some or all teeth and reduced the weight of the forearm by fusing most of the hand bones. Unlike the quadrupeds, the four-footed mammals, they developed neither paws nor hoofs.

Neither did bats, but they had to find different ways to lighten their bodies. Since bats needed fingers and teeth, major weight reduction was achieved in the leg structure. Shortening of the bone would have handicapped an insectivorous bat, for the length helps control the shape of the tail membrane as a flight surface and insect scoop. Instead, the upper leg bone, the femur, is very slender. The slimming is so extreme that it explains two of the most puzzling aspects of bat behavior—their ability to hang upside down and to move with crablike or reptilelike surface locomotion. Recent studies with engineering models show that columns of the proportion of a bat's femur will not support the weight of a bat's body. (The major exception, the vampire bats, have the heaviest known femurs among bats, and their ability to walk on all fours is well known.) By hanging upside down instead of standing, bats transfer the stress or force of compression on the legs to the ligaments as tension. Universally, bats either hang upside down or occupy horizontal crevices where external support is provided.

The wings of bats have fascinated scientists and at least one artist —John James Audubon. Though best known for his portraits of

American birds and his writings of *Ornithological Biography,* Audubon produced an impressive work on mammals, and he was particularly intrigued by the bats' "complete mastery of aerial navigation." As a result of his observations he concluded that "the wings of bats, rather than birds, offer the solution to aerial transport by man." He wrote, "If we look at the construction of the wings of bats, along with their internal structure, it will appear as if probably that should our own species ever attempt to fly through the air with wings they will have to be constructed on the principle belonging to these most curious animals."

Audubon's comment, made in 1846, was penciled in the corner of a drawing, one of a collection of watercolors that clearly establishes his keen interest in bats, a concern that went almost unnoticed for more than a century. His account of a bat-hunting episode concerning the eminent but eccentric naturalist Constantine Samuel Rafinesque while visiting the Audubons at Henderson, Kentucky, in 1818 is worth recounting.

"We had all retired to rest," related Audubon. "Every person, I imagined, was in a deep slumber, save myself, then all of a sudden I heard a great uproar in the naturalist's room." Rushing to Rafinesque's quarters, he found his guest running around the room stark naked "holding the handle of my favorite violin, the body of which he had battered to pieces against the walls in attempting to kill the bats which had entered by the open window, probably attracted by the insects flying around his candle.

"I stood amazed," Audubon went on, "but he continued jumping and running round and round, until he was fairly exhausted, when he begged me to procure one of the animals for him, as he felt convinced that they belonged to a new species. Although I was convinced to the contrary, I took the bow of my demolished Cremona, and administering a sharp tap to each of the bats as it came up, soon had specimens enough."

Audubon himself, in collaboration with the Reverend John Bachman, a Lutheran clergyman and naturalist, described a number of new species of bats. But, owing to a lack of critical data in his descriptions and to the disappearance of the original or "type" specimens, all but two of the names have passed into the oblivion of synonymy, the scientific graveyard of duplicate names.

Until 1951 this was virtually all that was known of Audubon's bat studies. Then, just as Alice Ford's handsome compilation of Audubon's drawings, *Animals: The Quadrupeds of North America*, was going to press, an unsuspected series of paintings of bats was found among the many hundreds of original Audubon watercolors of birds and mammals in the New-York Historical Society's priceless collection. Four fine drawings of the free-tailed and red bats were published in the Ford volume.

Later, as I studied the precious paintings in the Historical Society's vaults, I discovered a unique prize, an unknown painting of the specimen of the least brown bat, *Myotis leibii*, basis for the original description by Audubon and Bachman in 1840 and the rarest of bats until I started finding them in central Pennsylvania caves in 1931—an event that launched my lifelong interest in bats.

Wings. Since bats and birds solved the weight problem differently, it is not surprising that their wings are structured differently. In birds numerous wing bones are fused into a rather rigid supporting edge for the feathers. In bats the wing is shaped and supported by arm and finger bones.

The arrangement of the bones is clearly much like that of man. But it is modified—specialized—for supermaneuverability. A bat's wing bones are especially slender and light in weight. The four finger bones are extraordinarily lengthened while the thumb remains small and free of the wing's webbing. The first or index finger (actu-

John James Audubon's portrait of a free-tailed bat, one of a dozen bat paintings he never published. (Courtesy of New-York Historical Society, New York City)

ally the second digit), next to the thumb, supports (or forms the leading edge of) the wing.

The tips of the third, fourth, and fifth fingers provide the only support for the trailing edge of the wing, which is totally unlike the stiff leading edge. This rear edge of the wing membrane extends backward alongside the body and leg to the ankle or the nearest toe.

The thinness of a bat's wing must be seen to be appreciated. Essentially, it is made up of two layers of skin. When illuminated from behind, the membrane proves to be quite translucent, with blood circulation visible in major arteries and veins. Muscles and tendons can be seen. Juvenile bats as big as adults can be recognized by the large size and translucence of their still cartilaginous joints. When the bat settles into a resting position, certain wing muscles draw the membrane into regular puckers as the wing bones fold together. Though this large wing surface appears flimsy compared to a bird's more stabilized wing, it is capable of powerful strokes.

It is the wing's shape that determines flight characteristics, but the musculature, too, is important. Every wing stroke must be aerodynamically efficient, requiring the very minimum of energy. Muscles are so positioned that the bat can make amazingly swift changes of course, sudden maneuvers necessary for the pursuit and capture of insects highly adapted for evasive flight.

You can better appreciate the special modifications of bats by comparing their flight muscles with those of birds. In lightness and efficiency few birds can match them. In bats the weight of the breast or pectoral muscle is consistently less than 10 percent of the total body weight. For birds it averages 20 percent—as high as 33 percent for the deep-chested doves. This lightness of the breast muscle in bats is achieved by having the heavy, active portion away from the body. The section attaching to the breastbone is thin and tendonlike. Bats lack the prominent keel on the breastbone typical of most birds.

26

Meet the Bat

The flatness of a bat's chest has advantages, particularly in entering small cracks. Scientists believe that from the beginning of their evolution bats sought out constricted hiding places. Flatness of body was an advantage, and it has persisted. Most birds, on the other hand, perch out in the open. This has favored development of big, powerful breast muscles. Species of bats which fly long distances in open country instead of zigzagging through woodlands do have more powerful wing strokes, produced by larger, heavier muscles. Some of their maneuverability is sacrificed, but not enough to be critical.

In birds, flight muscles are braced solidly and almost immovably against the rib cage, as is the shoulder blade. Positioning of the flight muscles in bats is very different. Only one of the four muscles which control a bat's powerful downstroke is attached to the breastbone. Most muscles which control the wing-beat cycle are attached to the shoulder blade, which is not rigidly anchored but rocks rather loosely.

As in birds, the downstroke of a bat's wing produces the forward propulsion or thrust, the lift necessary for flight. The upstroke which elevates the wings is relatively passive and requires much less power. On the upstroke birds can spread some of their feathers and so reduce wind resistance. Bats, with their continuous wing surface, lack this advantage. Still, a bat's membrane wing has advantages of its own. The separate jointed sections of the bony framework of a bat's wing seem to mar its otherwise smooth contours. Actually, the various and changing angles of the finger bones affect the air flow across the highly cambered wings, possibly reducing the turbulence which would be expected at slow speeds. High-speed photography of bats in flight has revealed details of movements totally indiscernible to the unaided eye. For example, the trailing edge of the wing is seen to be quite flexible. During the downstroke the wing takes the shape of an airplane propeller. Lowering of the tail or interfemoral membrane influences flight, permitting a great increase in maneuverability.

27

*A long-tongued flower feeder in a New York zoo hovers for a split second for
a drink of man-made nectar. Many tropical bats lack the interfemoral or tail
membrane.*

Meet the Bat

Nectar-feeding bats have special problems. They need to hover in front of blossoms long enough to insert their long tongues into the tubular flowers. In terms of energy output, hovering is costly. But these bats have excessively cambered wings which produce high lift at low speeds. For them, level flight is less efficient but probably needs to be maintained for only short periods. They are not long-distance fliers as a rule.

There is no doubt that a bat's wing is marvelously specialized, highly suited for the special style of flight dictated by its food preferences and by the kinds of places where the food can be found. But the wing may be surprisingly useful in other ways. Bats can use their "hand-wing" like a baseball glove. High-speed pictures of a bat pursuing a flying insect have sometimes shown the bat appearing about to suffer a near miss. Then the pictures show that at the last moment the bat reaches out with a wing tip and sweeps in the insect, carrying it directly to its mouth or, momentarily, to the pouch formed by the tail membrane, from which it can easily be transferred to the mouth. Flying foxes use a pair of protruding claws on each wing to ascend tree trunks and travel along branches faster than their feet would carry them. Insectivorous bats use their clawed thumbs in moving around inside wall and roof spaces or inside cave crevices. The thumbs can also be used as "sky hooks" if a female bat needs to assume a hammock-type position while her baby is being born. Vampire bats have thumbs so large that they can serve as forelegs. The folded wing can even execute a good crawl stroke if the bat happens to get dunked. Wings also help regulate a bat's temperature. They serve as a sort of cocoon, conserving heat when a bat hangs in the open in cool weather, and they can radiate excessive heat generated in flight.

Ears. Horses, rabbits, and many other mammals have the ability to "point" their ears to concentrate on some highly directional or moving sound source. Considering the importance of pulse echoes to

29

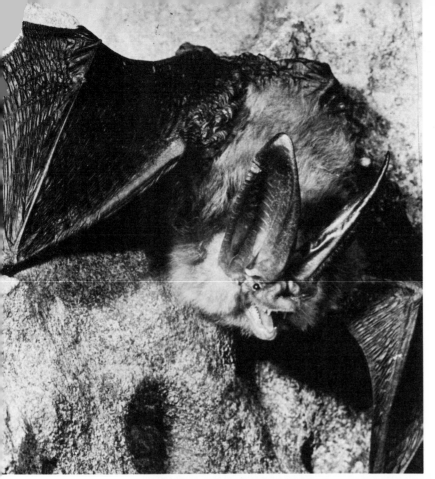

Eastern subspecies of the big-eared bat, Plecotus townsendii, *are threatened by repeated disturbance, which may drive them from their cave roosts. (Roger W. Barbour)*

Curling ears back may avoid injury or reduce water loss from the large, thin surfaces.

The tragus or earlet is found only in echolocating bats. In this Acadian bat, Myotis keenii, *it is very slender.* *(Roger W. Barbour)*

microbats in navigating and insect pursuit, it isn't surprising that they have relatively mobile ears. (The ears of the nonecholocating megabats are virtually immobile.)

The ear of most species of *Myotis* is relatively small, but slight variations in length and shape are noticeable and are consistent enough for scientists to rely upon them in differentiating among species. So, too, are differences in the shape of a fleshy projection called the tragus or earlet, which rises in front of the ear opening. It is suspected that the tragus plays some part in echolocation, although just how it operates remains unknown.

For most people, the most intriguing thing about bats is Griffin's discovery—echolocation—the first example in the animal kingdom. Thus, the structure of the bat's ear is particularly fascinating.

Once scientists realized that bats navigated by hearing echoes, not by sensing differences in air pressure, and that the echoes resulted

31

This wide-awake bat sees well in dim light but echolocates before taking off. (Roger W. Barbour)

from sounds produced by the vocal apparatus, not from wing movements as was once believed, other important questions were generated. How can a bat send out, with extreme rapidity, a series of quite intense, loud signals or pulses and simultaneously detect and analyze the faint echoes? Scientists puzzled over this—and over the fact that the intense sounds produced in the larynx of the bat, traveling through the skull directly to the inner ear, didn't drown out the faint echoes by which the bat must navigate.

Research done at Yale University by O. W. Henson, Jr., and associates revealed that the middle inner-ear muscles contract before each sonar pulse is broadcast. This greatly reduces the impact on the bat's ear. Then the muscles relax before the echo arrives, so the full, though relatively weak, signal is received. Other research on the

The European greater horseshoe bat, Rhinolophus ferrumequinum, *emits a narrow beam of sonar pulses through its hornlike nose, not its mouth. (J. H. D. Hooper)*

structure of the middle and inner ear cleared up the other puzzle regarding transmission of sound through the skull. Middle and inner ear structure is solidly fused to the skulls of most mammals. Not so in bats: The critical auditory structures are surrounded by fatty connective tissue or by blood-filled sinuses. This floating isolation evidently reduces bony conduction of sound both from the larynx and between the ears.

Eyes. The myth "blind as a bat" has been disproved. Although the eyes of microbats are smaller than those of the fruit-eating megabats, they are functional. There is speculation that much of their migration may be visually guided.

Echolocation. Ordinarily, sonar navigation is totally without vision and involves pulses of very highly pitched sound produced at short intervals, usually from a few to 200 times per second, each pulse lasting no more than a few thousandths of a second. The pulse rate, the duration of each pulse, and the pitch or frequency of the sound produced can be varied within limits according to the needs of the moment. For example, a bat foraging for insects will use a low pulse rate of longer bursts of sound at a high frequency for navigation and search until it locates an insect. Then the pulse rate is greatly increased, the pulses shortened and their pitch lowered to provide more precise guidance until the insect is caught.

The actual capture of the moving target involves a trade-off of sorts. Compensating for the biologically difficult effort to target the moving insect precisely is the fact that a "near miss" is still a "success" because, as we noted earlier, the bat can sweep in the insect with its wing tip; it doesn't need to stab it in full flight with its teeth.

Alvin Novick relates the design of sonar pulses to wing anatomy and flight pattern and speed. Bats, like *Tadarida,* that fly swiftly and straight over open country usually use "very intense and highly frequency-modulated orientation pulses. The intensity presumably is designed to increase their effective inspection range in an environment in which echoing surfaces are rare." In contrast, bats which dodge and hover in jungle thickets or temperate woodlands on shorter, broader wings "generally produce sonar signals of low intensity and short duration, often lacking frequency modulation."

Insect Countermeasures. Observers of insect pursuit by bats noted that certain moths foiled their would-be predators by evasive flight maneuvers. In *Listening in the Dark: The Acoustical Orientation of Bats and Man,* Griffin describes "The War between the Bats and the Moths" as an example of the widespread evolutionary "arms race" between predator and prey. While the auditory organs of insects are totally unlike the ears of vertebrates such as bats, laboratory tests prove that some insects are sensitive to sound in the high-frequency range used by bats. Many moths react to such actual or simulated sound pulses by going into an erratic flight pattern or by diving directly to the ground, where they remain motionless until the danger has passed.

One group of moths, the *Arctiidae,* is able to produce soft, ultrasonic clicks. At first interpreted as a method of jamming the bat's echolocation guidance system, the clicking sounds are now believed to serve as a warning: "You know from experience that I taste bad; leave me alone." Any bat that recalls the bitter experience of a previous encounter with this type of moth immediately abandons the pursuit. Actually the bat may be passing up a tasty morsel. Researchers have discovered that certain species of edible moths mimic the clicks of the bitter moths and are swallowed readily by captive bats as long as the moths are silent.

Identifying Bats. Although this book was not designed to enable you to identify all of the forty species of North American bats, the photo-

SIZE RANGE OF SOME NORTH AMERICAN BATS

FAMILY, GENUS AND SPECIES	COMMON NAME	MILLIMETERS (1 inch = 25 mm)	
		FOREARM	WINGSPAN
FAMILY VESPERTILIONDAE			
Pipistrellus hesperus	Western pipistrelle	27–33	191–215
Pipistrellus subflavus	Eastern pipistrelle	31–35	208–256
SMALL-SIZED *Myotis*			
Myotis leibii	Least brown bat	28–30	212–248
Myotis californicus	California myotis	29–36	210–250
MEDIUM-SIZED *Myotis*			
Myotis lucifugus	Little brown bat	34–41	222–270
Myotis austroriparius	Southeastern myotis	36–41	238–270
Myotis sodalis	Indiana bat	35–41	240–267
LARGE-SIZED *Myotis*			
Myotis grisescens	Gray bat	40–46	275–300
Myotis velifer	Cave myotis	43–47	280–315
Eptesicus fuscus	Big brown bat	42–51	325–350
Euderma maculatum	Spotted bat	48–51	325–350
Lasiurus borealis	Red bat	35–45	290–350
Lasiurus cinereus	Hoary bat	46–58	380–410
FAMILY MOLOSSIDAE			
Tadarida brasiliensis	Free-tailed bat	36–46	290–325
Tadarida macrotis	Big freetail	58–64	417–436
Eumops glaucinus	Eastern mastiff bat	57–66	470
Eumops perotis	Western mastiff bat	72–82	530–570

The interfemoral membrane of the hoary bat, Lasiurus cinereus, *is heavily furred. The smaller Hawaiian hoary bat is on the U.S. Endangered Species List.*

graphs will help you recognize a good many of the species most likely to be encountered. Since few pictures give any useful clue to the size of the bat, metric measurements (1 inch = 25 millimeters), which are universally used in bat identification, are given in the accompanying chart for some of the most common or most notable species.

The list includes less than half of the species known in the United States. In size, the others fall within these extremes.

The range in sizes of bats is important. The severity of their bite is related to their size. Small teeth and limited jaw muscle power make it unlikely that the bites of pipistrelles and small *Myotis* species will penetrate a person's skin. Bats the size of the big brown and the hoary, however, can, and often do, draw blood if they are given the opportunity to bite—and several species are larger than these. Since all species of mammals are believed capable of contract-

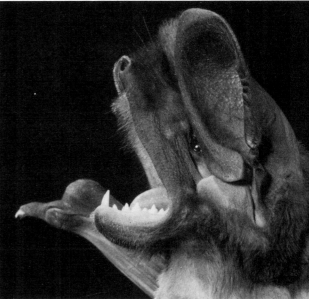

The western mastiff bat, Eumops pero-
tis, *largest in the United States, needs
a free fall of 6 feet to become airborne;
the smallest, the western pipistrelle, is
a slow, weak flier but can take off from
almost any surface. (Roger W. Barbour)*

*The call of a mastiff bat can be heard
at least half a mile away. (Roger W.
Barbour)*

The desert pallid bat, Antrozous pallidus, *sometimes lands to catch scorpions, insects, and lizards. (Roger W. Barbour)*

ing and transmitting rabies, it is clear that handling any bat with bare hands is hazardous. This warning cannot be overemphasized. Don't handle bats or other wild or strange mammals. In case of a bite the animal must be laboratory tested if you are to avoid a painful series of inoculations.

Bats the world over, and particularly those in the tropics, show great diversity in the foods they select while providing for their energy needs. In the United States, however, all but three species,

In the United States the leaf-nosed bat, Macrotus waterhousii, *is found only near the Mexican border. (Roger W. Barbour)*

The long-tongued bat, Leptonycteris sanborni, *reaches southern Arizona and New Mexico when desert plants are in bloom. (Roger W. Barbour)*

Little brown bats are scattered so widely in countless caves in winter and in summer nursing colonies that they are not threatened, as are great concentrations of Indiana and gray bats. (Roger W. Barbour)

which reach the Southwest from larger populations to the south, live exclusively on insects.

The Four Seasons. Seasonal change is recognized as a powerful influence on the lives of all plants and animals, but some are affected more than others. In bats, the cyclic effects of such change are especially notable on those species which spend part or all of the year in the northern temperate zone. It is commonly understood, of course, that the climatic evidence of the calendar seasons appears cross-country at different times, based on latitudinal isotherms—bands of similar temperature. In Indiana and north central Kentucky, Stephen R. Humphrey and his cooperators studied hundreds of populations of little brown bats, *Myotis lucifugus*. For convenience we shall adopt Humphrey's revision of the seasons as he experienced them in this study area:

Spring (April 1–May 31) includes spring movements and most of the gestation period.

Summer (June 1–July 25) includes the birth, maternal care, and development of the young and the first few days of their flight.

Fall (July 26–October 15) includes dispersal from the summer roosts, fall swarming behavior, and migration to wintering sites.

Winter (October 16–March 31) is the period of hibernation.

Spring

MIGRATING CANADA GEESE move northward in the wake of spring thaws as the average daily temperature reaches 35° F. Buds on the early-blossoming trees have been expanding for weeks before the temperature reaches 44° F. and the leaves finally unfold. For bats, spring comes when flying insects return to the air. Inside a cave unvarying darkness provides no visual cues to rouse the bats from their months-long dormancy; moreover, temperature fluctuation deep in the cave is minimal and humidity is constant. Rather than the direct indicators of light and warmth that quicken most plants and animals, the stimulus for bats is indirect: hunger. Even at the minimal winter usage of energy, depletion of fat deposits in the bat's body has by now become critical. Bats which have been disturbed frequently during the winter—particularly young bats with less fat in reserve—may not be able to survive until insects are flying outside. For bats, energy conservation is a way of life.

Once roused, the bats begin to make short "light sampling" flights into the dimly lit entrance zone. Studying emergence patterns in a colony of 2,500 to 3,000 *Myotis velifer,* the cave myotis, in Arizona, Earl G. McKinley noted that a few bats would fly outside for about five minutes. This was the period of the evening when atmospheric conditions were changing rapidly. The mass emergence was multiple triggered, McKinley decided: primarily by the level of light intensity

In the spring, cave bats give up a safe environment: dark, cool, and quiet.

and secondarily by the *rate of change* of ambient, air temperature and atmospheric pressure. For undetermined reasons, on some nights the column of bats flew west, on other nights east; but on all nights collisions with many inanimate objects at heights of 5 to 15 feet above the ground were frequent. Apparently, the column was too dense to permit maneuvering away from echolocated obstructions.

The first flights of the season usually last fifteen to twenty-five minutes, depending largely on the number of insects flying. Insect distribution so early is likely to be spotty. Hunting is best over water where insects may be transforming from aquatic pupae into winged adults. Bats quickly locate the areas of abundance and concentrate their activities there.

The insects a small bat consumes in a night amount to 20 to 30 percent of the bat's weight, but much of the food is useless to the bat. For fruit bats it may be in the form of structural cellulose from plants; for insect eaters, chitin from exoskeletons. Both types of food contain long-chain molecules indigestible for most vertebrates. Vampire bats, however, nightly swallow their weight in blood, but much is in the form of excess water. They derive their energy from a relatively small portion of the blood—a very rich food—and quickly excrete the excess.

Until recently, attempts to determine exactly what kinds of insects bats eat have been disappointing. Unlike birds, reptiles, and amphibians, which swallow much of their prey whole, bats chew theirs into tiny pieces. They eat only the soft abdominal sections of the larger insects, discarding the harder wings and heads, the parts on which most identifications depend. A bat's teeth are more numerous and specialized than those of most other mammals, except shrews and man. They make mincemeat of the chitinous exoskeletons of insects. The waste material, guano, is eventually eliminated as fecal pellets and is attacked by the larvae of dermestid beetles, which further reduce the already small fragments.

Food Gathering. Public acceptance of the bat's place in the natural world springs chiefly from the increasing realization that bats represent the nocturnal counterpart to certain bird families such as flycatchers, swallows and martins, and nighthawks whose insect-pursuing activities have been long-observed and widely documented. Observation of the insect predation practiced by bats, however, has been minimal, and until recently has been meagerly documented. But since mosquitoes are so multitudinous and annoying, we have assumed that they must be a prime source of bat fodder.

In the early 1920s a Texas physician, Dr. Charles A. R. Campbell, built towers designed to house thousands of bats, leading, he said, to controlling yellow-fever-carrying mosquitoes and providing considerable income through the sale of bat guano for fertilizer. Many communities bought blueprints and constructed towers in Texas,

Towers built for bats failed to draw them from established Texas roosts.

Florida, California, and Louisiana, as well as in undrained portions of the Pontine Marshes, near Rome, Italy.

In 1938 I visited the only tower known to house bats, near San Antonio. A colony of freetails, *Tadarida,* had moved in when their roost, a nearby barn, had been torn down. Other efforts, even with generous applications of odoriferous guano, proved unsuccessful. Government experts, when approached, discouraged further tower-building by pointing out the obstacles to persuading bats to give up

45

Dispossessed bats moved into one tower.

accustomed roosts and by their findings that these free-tailed bats did not eat *any* mosquitoes.

The revelation came from painstaking analysis of guano from nearby *Tadarida* roosts, and it has been verified by later studies that show that 90 to 95 percent of their food consists of micromoths, 5 to 9 mm in length. These moths are agricultural pests, so the annual consumption of hundreds of tons by bats must constitute a sizable economic benefit—a factor that influenced a major Air Force decision in the 1970s, as we shall learn later.

But what about other kinds of bats elsewhere in this country? Until fairly recently, the only other substantial information came from Cornell University, where William J. Hamilton, Jr., reported in 1932 on his painstaking examination of 2,200 fecal pellets of *Eptesicus,* the big brown bat. Hamilton also found no mosquito remains, but he didn't find moths either. He identified fragments of beetles, wasps and flying ants, and various flies—in total, 76 percent of the insects he recognized. His study didn't generate much enthusiasm for research on bat menus.

After photographers at the Massachusetts Institute of Technology demonstrated the speed and efficiency of insect pursuit by bats such as the little brown and the red bat—two fruit flies per second—scientists began to collect bats in the act of eating insects. Stomach contents were preserved and later compared with complete insects or with tremendously enlarged photographs of insect parts made with a scanning electron microscope. Anthony Ross of Arizona Western College

When curled forward, a bat's interfemoral membrane may scoop in an insect caught with a wing tip, or it may cradle the infant at birth.

found some bats with stomachs crammed with a single species of insect, or several layers of just a few kinds.

A much more diversified diet characterizes the food selection by the cave myotis, *M. velifer,* which frequently shares the same roosts with the freetail. In the gypsum cave country of southwestern Kansas, Thomas H. Kunz found that beetles constituted 37.4 percent of the diet; leafhoppers and related insects were second, with 17.9 percent; crane flies and other Diptera were third, with 14.4 percent; and moths were fourth, with 11.6 percent. The size of the prey varied from tiny midges less than 4 mm long to beetles up to 22 mm, but averaging 12 mm. Investigators agree that bats of various sizes "prefer" to prey upon insects whose size falls within a range or class that can be handled efficiently—the bigger the bat, the larger the insect the bat's jaws will accommodate. Preferred or available, prey also depends on a bat's wing design. The freetail's narrow wings are adapted to fast, direct flight, which works well where swarms of micromoths are encountered. Bats like *Myotis* have shorter but broader wings, better for the zigzag pursuit of more scattered insects of many types.

In Iowa, Kunz timed emergence of various species of bats and the duration of their feeding in relation to the time when certain insect species are most active. He found that little browns feed early, on a large but diversified insect population that is active in the first few hours after sunset. Species that prey on moths feed most heavily around midnight, because these insects are relatively inactive earlier. A resurgence of insect activity before dawn brings out certain species of bats which take advantage of the chance for an additional snack before retiring to their daytime roosts. Their total feeding time per night may amount to not more than two to three hours when insects are abundant.

Selective or Random Feeding? Do bats make a deliberate choice among the insects flying in areas where they feed most frequently?

Bats are hard enough to see in the dark, let alone the tiny insects, other than man-hunting mosquitoes. Decades ago, entomologists began to supplement their hand-net collecting with large portable traps employing fans to suck flying insects into containers. This was more thorough than light traps, which attracted fewer insects and only kinds that responded positively to certain wavelengths of light.

In 1973 Edward R. Buchler placed a suction trap next to the Japanese mist net he was using to catch little brown bats as they came to feed at a pond just 100 yards from their roost in a building at Rockefeller University's field station at Millbrook, New York. When he compared the insects he trapped at the place and time that the bats foraged with those in the bats' stomachs, he noted some surprising differences.

If the bats were pursuing a random hunting strategy, taking anything from a gnat measuring 3 mm (about the minimum detectable with the bat's FM closeup echolocation cry) to mayflies at 9 mm (wingspread 18 mm), a miscellaneous assortment of as many as seventeen insect types might have appeared in the bat stomachs. Among these, mayflies in the suction trap samples amounted to 1.2–2.4 percent, but an astonishing 81 to 100 percent in the stomachs! Traps turned up mosquitoes in proportions of 2.1–4.7 percent, but only one bat ate any. It appears that while *Myotis* at times may prey upon any suitably sized insect that happens to be flying, at a particular time and place they may be specialists to an extreme degree. Buchler believes that the echolocation pulses of bats enable them to distinguish "subtle nuances" from the echoes of different insects, including body texture, wing-beat frequency, and flight pattern and speed. High palatability or ease of capture may act as positive reinforcers.

Tracking Bats. Movement of a bat through a particular passage can be detected by an electric eye. This was possibly first realized in Buffalo, New York, when mysterious burglar alarms turned out to be triggered by bats flying in the building. Geiger counters have been used to locate bats tagged with radioactive cobalt in spaces where they could not be seen. Reflective bat bands or tape, when located and held within the beam of visible or infrared light, have permitted brief periods of tracking of the carriers. Electronic "bat detectors" permit listening in on echolocating bats as they navigate and pursue insects.

Flights of vampire bats carrying miniature radio transmitters have revealed the location of the caves from which they launch their attacks on livestock in Tropical America, while more innocent foraging flights of big brown bats have been observed briefly when the bats wore battery-powered pinlights. Smaller bats, however, have been unable to carry such heavy loads.

In pursuing his studies of insect prey selection by little brown bats, Buchler wanted to know exactly where a bat was going and what it was doing in the dark. He came up with a revolutionary technique —cementing onto the bat a chemiluminescent tag that will glow brightly for hours and will be visible on moonless nights from as much as 475 yards away. The "tag"—actually a hollow glass sphere 10 mm in size or smaller—is filled with a mixture of two ingredients available in commercial "light sticks" sold as an emergency light source. The cold light produced is unaffected by water—it has been used to track frogs and turtles—and is nontoxic.

Buchler wanted to track young bats to see how they improved their insect-catching skills and whether their behavior differed noticeably from that of adults. It does—flight is often less adept and flights are briefer. The young frequently land in trees for short periods, probably to rest. One particular tree at the edge of a dense forest was regularly used as a flyway stopover. Many adult and young little browns frequently landed on the tree trunk, which may have had significance beyond being simply a resting station. Buchler detected a faint "batty" smell on the bark at the elevation where the bats

A pallid bat, Antrozous, *carrying a chemiluminescent capsule was observed throughout a half-mile flight in the Nevada desert. Glass bubbles are now used, since gelatin capsules leak the toxic chemical, killing the bat.*

usually landed—probably from urine and/or scent-gland secretions—but he is still speculating on its social significance. Another original observation was that his light-tagged young bats often used less energy in insect pursuit than the strong-flying adults. Juvenile bats often hung from a tree trunk until they detected a close-flying insect, at which they launched out in pursuit, then returned to their original perch for all the world like a phoebe or one of its fly-catching relatives. It is clear that a whole new field of nocturnal behavior study is made possible by the use of the luminescent bubbles.

Flower Bats. The three species of flower-feeding bats which enter the extreme southwestern United States each spring from Mexico are the least frequently seen of our bats. Each has a small triangular flap of skin rising from the tip of the snout, but it is the long, slender nose and the greatly extendable tongue that give the common names of long-nosed or long-tongued bat to all three species. Unlike many insectivorous species which bite readily, the flower bats are noted for their gentleness.

The wanderings of flower bats are not well understood, but these bats are capable of surprising, unexpected appearances. In 1946 there was an invasion of *Choeronycteris* in San Diego, groups of them taking up residence in houses, garages, and patios. But usually they are hard to find. The only colony of *Leptonycteris nivalis* that has been found in the United States is in Big Bend National Park, Texas, where at times a colony numbering as many as 8,000 has been seen in a remote cave about 1½ miles high on Mount Emery's peak. Students of bats do encounter Sanborn's long-tongued bat—*L. sanborni*, the third flower-eating species—with some regularity in certain caves and mines in parts of the Southwest where alluvial soils at the base of mountains support agave, yucca, saguaro, and organ-pipe cactus. It is the blossoming of these plants in late spring which triggers the migration of the flower bats from central Mexico as the blooming of nectar-producing plants there comes to an end.

The flowers have an amazing variety of adaptations seemingly designed to alert and assist these bats in their feeding. More than 130 species of plants have been identified as possessing floral "invitations" that bats recognize and approach. These visits are necessary for the fertilization of the plants. The elongated noses and tongues of the flower bats are, in turn, well adapted to extracting the nectar from deep within the tubular flowers. A breakthrough in photography—almost three-dimensional pictures made by a stereoscan electron microscope—provided the first clear images of a multitude of scales and bristles on the tongue of *Leptonycteris*.

But how do you make a bat out of sugar and water? Anyone assuming that these bats could survive on a diet of nectar alone was overlooking the well-established protein requirement for mammalian growth and development. By analyzing the stomach contents and the guano of hundreds of flower-visiting bats, Donna Howell, a graduate student at Arizona State University, determined that only 70 to 75 percent of their diet was nectar. Something else showed up in the analyses—pollen. Not very much, but pollen is so highly nutritious that a little bit is enough to furnish the roughly 10 percent protein that mammals other than bats are known to require. No doubt it is the nectar that lures the bat; but in terms of the plant's need pollen has top priority, and these plants are equipped to deliver it to the bats. In the first place, these plants are night bloomers, and bats are nocturnal feeders. The plants are easily found, for they have flowers white or light enough to be visible at dusk or in moderate moonlight, and therefore the blooms stand out in the dark. And they "smell out" as well, having a scent resembling the distinctive musky odor of bats,

Many tropical plants "invite" visits from nectar-seeking long-tongued bats and benefit from cross-pollination. (Bruce Hayward)

from the same butyric acid present in rancid butter and in the glandular secretions of some bats. Springlike anthers slap their pollen against the bat's head and neck as it probes the flower. These pollen grains are abundant, large, and sticky.

Further indication of the sophisticated interrelationships between bat and plant came when Howell compared the hairs of insectivorous bats with those of her pollinating flower bats. Instead of the smooth-scaled hair of *Myotis* and other insect eaters, these flower eaters had rough-surfaced hair, with projecting scales of several sorts. Sticky pollen grains in quantity catch on the projections. Sometimes a bat is so heavily dusted with the golden pollen of the century plant, agave, that it appears to be yellow. Later the bat will scrape this pollen loose with sweeping claw movements and, by preening with its rough-surfaced tongue, it will swallow the pollen. Such preening may have started as a purely grooming act, but it is now the way the bat gets all or nearly all of its protein.

Like most pollen grains, those gathered by flower bats have a tough coat, the exine, a waxy, waterproof stuff. This would pass undigested through the gut of most vertebrates. But the same pollen sprouts quickly in warm sugar-water solutions—just what is present as the combined pollen and nectar mixes with warm saliva on the way to a bat's stomach. There the dilute hydrochloric acid dissolves out the protein and prepares it for digestion. Howell also determined that these pollens are twice as high in nitrogen as nonbat flowers and that they are particularly high in the amino acid tyrosine, which is critically important in embryonic and infant growth.

The Mystery of Migration. A good deal has been learned about migration routes and distances through the recapture of banded bats. We know very little about what happens en route between winter and summer quarters and on the return trip, but it is now recognized that certain caves are used quite regularly for brief stopovers. But how do bats navigate? Since echolocation pulses are generally ineffective in producing echoes from beyond 100 yards, long flights must be based on different cues. Vision may be involved.

Comparison of successful returns of blindfolded and of untreated Indiana bats from distances up to 200 miles seems to support the conclusion that inability to see is a handicap. Radio tracking of bats for distances up to 10 miles showed bats with unimpaired vision flying to their home caves with remarkable directness. Blindfolded bats flew more slowly and less directly, but at 35 miles both groups flew randomly.

Evidently visual familiarity with the home terrain influences short flights. When close to home, bats apparently rely on spatial memory —"fifty flaps ahead, then dip down to the right" might get a bat repeatedly through a cave on down a woods road—but an unexpected obstacle, such as a spelunker or a mist net, might cause a collision and force the bat to pay attention to the echoes returning from familiar and unfamiliar surfaces. What would the bats be looking at on long-distance flights? The moon and stars? Possibly; birds do. Bats, however, are not known to have the necessary visual acuity to do so. But the general brightness patterns of the night sky—the Milky Way, for example—might offer directional guidance. Search for the sensory basis for demonstrated migratory skills remains one of the greatest challenges for inquiring scientists.

Arrival of the Freetails. The tremendously abundant freetails, *Tadarida brasiliensis,* fly as much as 800 to 1,000 miles from wintering roosts in the Mexican lowlands south of the Tropic of Cancer to cave roosts in Arizona, New Mexico, and Oklahoma. The most astonishing thing about a flight of freetails is its size and suddenness. At about midnight on April 22, 1958, R. B. Davis and other scientists from the University of Arizona watched several million bats drop out of the night sky into Frio Cave in central Texas within a space of ten

Free-tailed bats reach Carlsbad Caverns in May after flying as much as 800 miles from Mexico.

minutes. Earlier that day, they had seen only a few dozen bats in the cave. Farther south, at the Cave of the Tiger in Sonora, Mexico, no bats were present on March 24, 1962—but the next morning approximately 100,000 were seen, 85 percent of them males. Among freetails the females migrate later. At Carlsbad Caverns National Park in New Mexico, Denny G. Constantine witnessed the arrival of several hundred thousand bats at midnight on May 15, 1956.

Constantine was the first to report bats flying at altitudes as much as 2 miles high—a fact confirmed twenty years later by radar. He believes that such high-level flights involve considerable stress because of greater exposure to solar radiation, low atmospheric pressure, and

This bat has been entombed for centuries on a stalagmite.

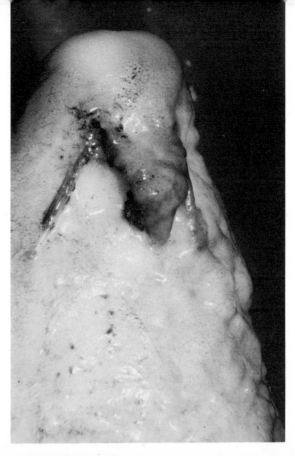

These bats died 19,000 years ago. (Note the size of bones and skulls revealed by the metric scale.)

The free-tailed bat is a strong flier. It is incredibly abundant but is beset by serious survival problems. (Roger W. Barbour)

low oxygen concentration. This may well be true of long migratory flights, but for nightly feeding forays high flights may be an energy efficient system for rapid dispersal of huge colonies to distant feeding grounds.

An additional hazard, Constantine noted, was the possibility of being caught by a severe storm. Survival of large numbers of migrating bats may depend on being able to locate emergency shelter quickly. On one occasion Constantine found great masses of freetails

58

hanging in full view on the sides of a building on a Texas college campus. Other transient groups often found shelter under wooden railroad bridges until these structures were replaced by less hospitable concrete and steel structures.

Die-offs Spur Studies. Serious studies of the bat population at Carlsbad were begun in 1956, after several large-scale die-offs of the bats there and elsewhere had been reported. Rabies had been found in the United States in 1953. Rabies-suspect bats were studied in the Southwest and elsewhere across the country. The two largest investigations, in Arizona and Kentucky, were financed by grants from the U.S. Public Health Service. A very substantial amount of our knowledge about the dynamics of bat populations, migration, and reproduction can be credited to the vigor and intensity of these studies. They will probably never be duplicated, for among other things they provided data that showed the incidence of rabies among bats to be very low.

Eagle Creek Cave. E. Lendell Cockrum and his associates at the University of Arizona banded bats at seventy localities in Arizona and New Mexico, and in Sonora and Chiapas, Mexico. Huge populations of freetails were found in four caves. By far the largest was in Eagle Creek Cave, 4 miles down a deep canyon in Greenlee County, Arizona. Late winter snow melt and late summer rains flood the canyon, but the cave is generally accessible when transient bats and a maternity colony are present—accessible but difficult to reach even with four-wheel drive vehicles. And then there is a steep 100-foot climb up the canyon wall to the imposing entrance.

In 1963 especially favorable light penetration on April 13 made it possible to see a population of *Tadarida* far greater than anyone had ever reported—possibly the largest that exists anywhere in the world. Adult bats blanketed the walls and ceiling of the single chamber,

Tens of thousands of freetails hit a double barricade of parallel wires and slide down a chute into cages in Arizona's Eagle Creek Cave. (Bruce Hayward)

which is 288 feet long, 65 feet wide, and 100 feet high. A large ceiling crack extending another 60 to 70 feet higher was lined with bats. Cockrum estimated the population to be as high as 50 to 60 million.

This was nearly two months before the time for *Tadarida* to bear young. Most of the bats were probably on their way to maternity roosts farther north, Cockrum believes, because much later in the season, in 1964, far fewer bats occupied the cave—only 100,000 on June 1, 250,000 the next morning, and 1,000,000 by June 3.

It was in Eagle Creek Cave that the greatest bat banding operation of all time took place. In a three-day session in early June 1963 Cockrum headed a team of twenty-five banders who marked 37,500 freetails, 90 percent of them pregnant females. Many of these bats were probably headed for Oklahoma. Recoveries of bats banded here established flight records of as much as 175 miles in no more than four nights and 85 miles in no more than two nights, at as much as 42.5 and 43.8 miles per night. From Carlsbad four banded freetails made the 500-mile flight to Oklahoma caves at approximately the same speed.

Dispersal from Northern Caves. From northern Florida to Missouri, Kentucky, and New England, cave bats are leaving their subterranean wintering quarters. Virtually every species except the big-eared *Plecotus townsendii* will be leaving, and even the big-eared will move to warmer portions of its year-round cave home. The huge concentrations of wintering gray bats, *Myotis grisescens,* will redistribute themselves in other caves as much as 300 miles to the north or northwest, with females seeking the warmest caves, males the coldest. No other eastern species chooses to spend the summer underground, although occasional bands of male Indiana bats, *Myotis sodalis,* are found wandering through certain caves in Mammoth Cave National Park in Kentucky.

These gray bats, Myotis grisescens, *will leave a cold Kentucky cave and fly to warmer nursery caves scattered over 10,500 square miles in three states.*

Spring

Where the female *sodalis* go has been one of the major mysteries of the bat world. They just vanished when they left their caves, primarily in eastern and central Kentucky. In 1973 Stephen R. Humphrey of the Florida State Museum, Gainesville, received a report of *sodalis* in hollow trees in Missouri, and the following year he verified the report with further observations, noting that the trees were along stream banks, very vulnerable to dam building and stream channelization projects. Wild river status, proposed for several streams in the *sodalis* nursery region, would have fringe benefits previously unanticipated—protection for an endangered species.

In New England at least, individual bats move swiftly once spring flights get under way. One little brown bat banded at a Vermont cave in April was recaptured 80 miles away after three nights. Most of the bats banded at Aeolus Cave, Vermont, move southeast in a rather narrow band leading to Cape Cod, 185 miles away. Some move northward into the Champlain Valley; a few scatter in other directions.

By the end of May the bats are gone from their wintering grounds. Whether it is highly nutritious pollen that lures some flower bats north of the Mexican border, or incredibly abundant micromoths that bring the multitudinous freetails to our vast Southwestern landscape, or highly diversified insect populations that draw hungry little brown bats and their kin from caves and other secret hibernacula to forage over woodland, farm, and town, all of them are driven by an urge to culminate the cycle of reproduction—giving birth to a new generation. As the end of spring approaches, the bats are nearing the end of their gestation period—fifty to sixty days for the little brown and seventy-seven to eighty-four days for freetails in Florida, but up to one hundred days in California. Insect populations reach a peak. Pregnant females reach their maximum weight, but they show no loss of aerial dexterity. They are the ones which will occupy our attention in the upcoming summer season.

63

Summer

ABOUT FIFTEEN MINUTES after sunset in the Southeast and in California, hundreds of free-tailed bats leave their roosts and begin to forage for insects. Most of them appear from beneath the roof edges of warehouses and lofts, and from barns and church steeples. In San Marcos, California, Philip Krutzsch clocked their departure from a church. He counted five bats a minute, a thousand in three hours. That was a small colony, of course—in more than a dozen caves in Texas, Oklahoma, New Mexico, and Arizona, maternity colonies of freetails number in the millions.

Flights from these Southwestern bat caves are truly spectacular. The first great flight of freetails I saw was at Carlsbad Caverns late in June 1938. I had spent a brief period in the huge maternity roost half a mile off the tourist trail trying to confirm the report of an estimated population of nearly nine million bats. Our presence probably disturbed them because they started flying from the cave early, about half an hour before sunset. Their departure was direct and swift as they headed for the Pecos River 40 miles away, at speeds estimated at 40 to 60 miles per hour. From a distance such a flight looks like smoke from a moving train and explains why some of these caves are known as "smoke holes."

Predators. As they leave their sheltered daytime roosts, the freetails have to run a gauntlet of predatory animals. The vulnerability of the bats depends largely on the size of the cave entrance. Bats forced to funnel through a constricted cave mouth may be snatched in mid-air by a leaping cacomistle (ringtail) or speared by a big snake. When some bats inevitably collide, a number of them fall to the ground. The barely heard thud of a downed bat is likely to be followed almost instantly by a louder thud as a furry predator pounces on its victim.

Outside the caves, other hazards exist—hawks and owls have gathered to take advantage of the aerial traffic jam. Owls—usually horned, screech, or barn—often roost just outside the entrance. At Carlsbad for many years a pair of horned owls waited for the nightly exit of the freetails. They would join the bats spiraling upward out of the cave, snatch one with their deadly talons, and fly to a ledge. There they would tear off the wings and head, then swallow the still warm carcass in a single gulp. Later the identity of the bat victim could be confirmed by examination of the skull found in the regurgitated pellet —a neat package of fur and bones.

Raccoons visit remote parts of many caves.

This screech owl waited in a dark cave entrance for bats to emerge.

The most conspicuous predators are hawks. In the 1930s as many as six peregrine falcons were seen diving into the bat column emerging from Ney Cave, Texas, before dusk. The swifter hawks—occasional prairie falcons and kestrels as well as peregrines—seemed to have a higher batting average than the slower but commoner red-tailed hawks which are attracted by major bat flights. Success of a hawk's efforts may be as low as one catch in ten dives. The hawks disappear before dark but often reappear about dawn. In southern Oklahoma fifteen Mississippi kites were seen wheeling in circles, twisting and diving into a column of freetails returning to Reed Cave between 5:00 and 7:30 A.M. While aerial pursuit of bats is dramatic and spectacular, most experts believe that such predation has no appreciable effect on the huge populations of freetails.

Other Cave Bats. West of the Mississippi a good many small caves, mines, and quarry tunnels are occupied by bats in summer—most often the cave myotis, *M. velifer,* but including the big-eared *Plecotus* and *Antrozous,* along with *Eptesicus,* the big brown. One such bat

66

Freetails form a column as they leave a nursery cave at dusk to forage thirty or more miles away. (Courtesy of Texas Park and Wildlife Department)

cave was reported to be on the Prassel Ranch in the Edwards Plateau of central Texas. Ken Dearolf and I followed a local guide upstream along a small river to the cave entrance, then waded into the tunnel-like passage. There had been heavy showers in the area earlier in the day, but now it was clear outside. And the stream flowed *out* of the cave. It was safe, we figured, though I had heard of underground streams in Kentucky flooding twenty-four hours after storms occurred in distant areas. In West Virginia I was 60 miles from a dry cave the day a cloudburst flooded it and drowned two spelunkers.

But this stream was clear, 15 feet wide and 3 feet deep. The rock bottom—no mud—did suggest scouring action, but it made for good walking and good observation of aquatic life.

We were out of sight of the entrance when we first heard a distant rumbling sound. It must have been coming from far ahead along the winding cave passage, we thought, but in a few seconds the sound increased to a disturbing dull roar. We thought of climbing out of the stream to higher ledges or upper rooms—but there weren't any. This was just a water-carrying conduit. The cave had no doubt been dissolved out of the soluble limestone rock while the area lay beneath the water table. But once surface erosion had cut deepening valleys and lowered the water table, the subway system had further developed into intermittent subsurface drains.

And now, we realized, it was draining with sudden vigor. We were as hopelessly trapped as motorists crossing a dry desert arroyo are when a wall of water descends upon them. This sounded like an approaching subway train. Then, from around a bend, it was upon us— hundreds of bats! Hundreds of "silent-winged" bats crowded the tunnel, creating waves of reverberating sounds of a magnitude I still can't quite believe.

Separate Roosts. By early summer male and female bats have found separate quarters, sometimes scores of miles apart. In general, the

A colony of the cave myotis can produce reverberations along a cave passage.

These big brown bats in a Delaware attic retreat to cooler spaces if the temperature climbs above 104° F.

males have chosen cooler locations, the females warmer ones. But the temperature in any summer location will be far higher than in any hibernating site. This transfer can involve the greatest temperature extremes that any vertebrate animal is known to undergo. Within a few months bats that survived a subfreezing temperature of 20° F. may live in a sun-baked attic, where they have been known to survive peak temperatures of 131° F. In California a colony of the yuma myotis was found in a barn where the air temperature sometimes reached 122° F. in midafternoon. In the morning they could be found clustered at the top of a beam just beneath the roof. When the temperature there reached 104° F., the bats began to move down to the bottom of the beam. If the temperature rose still higher they gradu-

Little brown bats returned to this Pennsylvania roost repeatedly when carried away as far as eighty-five miles.

ally departed to other, cooler parts of the barn, but they returned before nightfall to their original roosting sites.

High nursery temperature has definite benefits. It makes faster digestion and milk production possible for the adult females, and it promotes rapid digestion and growth of the infant bats.

Bats of virtually all species are intolerant of disturbance in the nursery refuge. In Indiana, Humphrey located fifty colonies of little brown bats, *Myotis lucifugus,* and found that single populations readily moved to alternate buildings at times of disturbance or excessive heat. One abandoned farmhouse we visited in eastern Pennsylvania had so many suitable roosting spaces beneath the loose clapboards that we succeeded only once in catching the nearly 500

71

female bats; they simply moved to other spaces, in areas we couldn't cover with our nets.

Birth of a Bat. On June 15 three of the pregnant little browns we had carried back to the museum each gave birth to a single infant bat. Parturition (birth) begins with the female hanging head up—the reverse of the usual resting position. The interfemoral membrane, curved forward into a cup or basket, receives the fetus as it emerges feet first. The mother tears off the enveloping membrane and the baby begins reaching with its feet, grasping and pulling on the mother's body, assisting in its own delivery. Birth is completed within fifteen to twenty minutes, but the umbilical cord remains intact, with blood circulating through it for perhaps another 10 minutes. The fetus would bleed to death if the cord were broken before it naturally dries out. It desiccates and breaks away soon afterward.

The young bat clings tightly to a nipple until it is about half grown, releasing it only when the mother is ready to go foraging. The baby hangs alone until the mother returns in about an hour. She licks the baby's face and lips, then resumes nursing. After about two weeks the half-grown baby leaves its protected position, hidden beneath the mother's wing, and hangs beside her. The immature little brown has woolly, sooty gray fur, quite different from the glossy fur and yellowish undersides of the adult. The weight of the babies at birth ranged from 1.45 to 1.55 grams.

In most bat roosts dead babies will be found on the floor beneath the females. Generally any infant that falls is lost. There are, however, a few observations, some monitored by radioactive devices, of females retrieving fallen babies. Lost infants are evidently located and identified by the audible distress calls they make. Several scientists have reported that an infant separated from its mother calls continuously until she rejoins it.

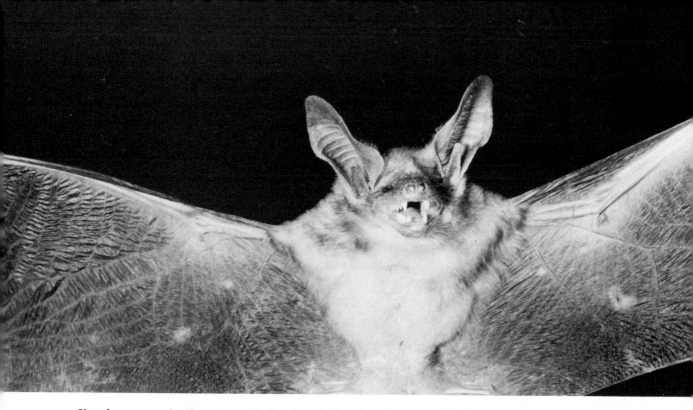

Vocal communication is well developed in the desert pallid bat, Antrozous pallidus.

Communication Calls. At the University of California at Los Angeles, Patricia Brown studied several laboratory-reared families of desert pallid bats, *Antrozous pallidus.* By taping their cries, then slowing the tape four to sixteen times, she was able to recognize different types of communication calls: isolation or *directive* calls, loud and rapid but short; *squabble* notes expressing minor annoyance when the bats are crowded, high-pitched and variable; and a harsh *irritation* buzz, accompanied by baring of teeth and spreading of wings. In addition to the audible emissions, there is ultrasonic *orientation* pulsing, emitted only when the bat is flying, crawling, or otherwise exploring its environment. Like most species—other than *Tadarida*—pallid bats feed only their own young and, if separated, respond only to them. Females responded to taped recordings made a week earlier, even though some change in the infant's call had occurred during that time. Brown determined that the first part of the calls of all infants is identical at

By the fifth week young pallid bats fly from roosts such as this rock shelter in search of insects, while flower bats drink the nectar of blossoms on cactus, agave, and other desert plants. (Roger W. Barbour)

the same stage of development but that the ending constitutes a vocal signature the mother recognizes.

Young *Myotis* of most species do poorly in captivity, but Brown's pallid bat babies were healthy—excellent subjects for daily growth observations. Fur isn't noticeable until the ninth day, and it is then that the ear—until then blocked by the fingerlike tragus—opens. Only now can the infant hear and answer its mother's directives, although it has been emitting an almost continuous series of peeps whenever it was separated from its mother.

Edwin Gould rates young pallid bats, *Antrozous*, as "altricial" because they are born naked, with eyes and ears closed. So are *Tadarida*, the freetails. Two tropical species studied by Gould were relatively mature at birth, or "precocial." Little brown bats are intermediate.

Bat Cave Rigors. Recognition of individual babies by their vocal signatures seems to account for the ability of bat mothers to quickly locate their own hungry infant among dozens or hundreds of babies in the nursery roost. But in the huge nursery colonies of freetails in Southwestern caves, a returning female might face the problem of finding her offspring among a million or more babies.

In Ney Cave, about 50 miles from the Bracken nursery cave, I have seen more than 10,000 square feet of cave wall blanketed with baby bats. All evidence points to the females operating as a nurse herd, available to the first babies that reach them as they land among the tapestry of young bats.

The temperature in the main bat chamber at Ney Cave was 95° F. —ideal for rapid growth of infant bats, but highly unpleasant for human visitors. As a safeguard against breathing rabies virus, airborne in urine and mucous droplets, we wore masks, almost intolerable in the heat—and made worse by the exertion in wading through soft guano, piled a yard deep in places between scattered limestone blocks on a steeply sloping cave floor.

75

Worst of all are the ammonia fumes generated by the decomposing guano. Constantine tells of suffering a glottis spasm after thirty minutes in a bat cave with an ammonia concentration of 195 ppm and having a similar attack after just a few minutes in a Mexican cave where ammonia concentrations measured 1,850 ppm. But *Tadarida* is adapted to life in such atmospheres. E. H. Studier, of the University of Michigan, attributes the bat's ability to endure thirty to fifty times the amount of fumes man can tolerate on the buffering action of the respiratory mucus made possible by absorbing greatly increased amounts of carbon dioxide. It is not known whether young bats are affected by the high ammonia concentration, but the bleaching action of ammonia on bat fur has long been recognized.

It is known that infant mortality is high in some caves, particularly in certain cool caves. In Carlsbad, Constantine rated the bat roost as barely acceptable because it was too cool—65° to 69° F.—but the presence of a *large* nursery population here keeps the temperature above the critical minimum for growth and development. In some years, however, too few bats use the nursery quarters and the cave remains too cool to be suitable for raising young bats.

Falls from roosting places account for much of the infant mortality observed in these caves. Some falls have been traced to neuromuscular disorders which weaken the infants' grip, an outcome of ingesting DDE—a chemical derivative of DDT—in the bat mother's milk. Another hazard exists in the form of hordes of tiny mites which spread up the cave walls to the bat roost and can seriously weaken the infants. But even a perfectly healthy infant that survives a fall without injury is doomed. Unless it is very close to a wall and can scramble quickly upward to a safe perch, it will be attacked and devoured by predacious insects—the larvae of dermestid beetles which nearly blanket the guano on the cave floor.

Development of young *Tadarida* is slower than among some other species, possibly because the newborn young are relatively immature,

Red bats and other tree dwellers probably move a number of times with their babies. (Leonard Lee Rue III from National Audubon Society)

as Gould noted, or perhaps because, with their narrow, pointed wings, they have more difficulty getting airborne, so may need more development before flying at an age of five weeks. *Antrozous*, another altricial type, also does not fly until it is five weeks old. Species of *Myotis* such as the little brown and the gray bat may fly in as little as three weeks. Patricia Brown's young *Antrozous* began preflight movements in the third week. This consisted of spreading and flexing their wings and pushing away from the vertical roosting surface.

The final week before the young can fly must be a very critical time for the lactating mother. The infant's need for nourishment must be especially great, but there must be some means for the mother to persuade it to release its hold. Unless she can dislodge her offspring long enough to replenish her own energy supply, she cannot survive until the young is weaned. Freetails do leave their young hanging in the cave, but the mother tree bat must leave her young hanging on a tree branch or carry her growing family clinging to her.

Solitary Species: the Tree Bats. In supreme contrast to colonial species like *Tadarida* whose nursery colonies often number in the millions,

77

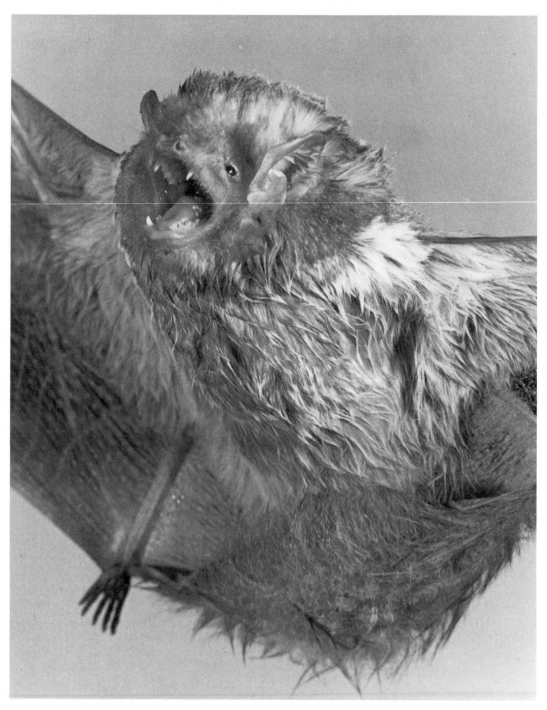

Red bats have rounded ears, a short tragus, and a heavily furred tail membrane.

the tree bats of the genus *Lasiurus* are the hermits of the bat world. Consequently, much less is known about their daily life. Most of man's encounters with them are accidental; but since they are especially vulnerable while weighted down by their multiple, nursing babies, summer is the time when they are most often seen.

Their daytime perches in trees may seem to be totally random choices. They are not. In Iowa, Georgia, and California, Constantine spent weeks searching for them in groves in open country. He located many scattered individuals, but consistently found them under almost identical circumstances along forest borders and fence lines. A typical site is protected from view from all directions except from below, permitting escape by dropping; has vegetation dense enough to block wind and blowing dust; has dark ground surface below, minimizing light reflection; and is located on the warm south or southwest side of the tree. Since such sites are occupied as individual nursery roosts

Young bats, particularly red bats, seem accident prone and perish on cactus thorns, barbed wire, and other hazardous objects.

for as much as fifteen hours between sunrise and sunset in June, selection is critically important.

Nursing female red bats, *Lasiurus borealis,* have a real handicap. They often bear as many as four young (the average is 3.2). There must be times when the babies weigh considerably more than the mother does. How many days she must be flightless while continuing to nurse them, no one knows. *Lasiurus cinereus,* the truly handsome hoary bat, only produces twins, so may have an easier time carrying them. On one occasion we captured a free-flying hoary bat weighing 27.1 grams (about one ounce) and carrying twins totaling 10.5 grams. Two other hoary mothers were taken while hanging in trees, not flying. The babies of one weighed half as much as the adult; in the second case, the babies weighed 15.1 and 16 grams respectively, precisely equal to the mother's weight. We banded them and hung them from a branch. In the morning they were gone.

There are still a few species of bats whose young have never been seen by scientists. The first birth ever seen of the rare spotted bat, *Euderma maculatum,* was observed and reported only a few years ago by David Easterla in Big Bend National Park, Texas, where he was a ranger-naturalist.

Return of the Males. In many nursery colonies a few adult males are present throughout the summer; 10 to 20 percent have been reported. The bulk of the males, however, have passed the time of their exclusion from the nursery colonies by moving from place to place in gypsy fashion. Now, as young bats swell the nursery populations, more and more adult males are found in the roosts—as high as 40 percent or more.

The males are back, but not for long. The whole colony is about to break up. The refuge has served its purpose: sheltering the pregnant females and providing a maternity ward for the birth of the babies, a nursery for the developing infants, and a base for their in-

The huge ears of this rare, spectacular spotted bat, Euderma maculatum, *are bright pink. (David A. Easterla)*

creasingly successful foraging flights. But these nursery sites are un-suited for permanent occupancy. Some are so warm that in winter they would make too great metabolic demands when no insect supply is available. Or they might be too cold to provide an above-freezing environment. It is time to go hunting for a winter home.

81

Banding of bats caught at this Pennsylvania cave in 1931 sparked interest in the life of bats.

Autumn

SPELUNKERS FOUND Schofers Cave, near Kutztown in southeastern Pennsylvania, small but fascinating. An underground lake generally blocked the most distant room to all but scuba divers. On repeated trips we had found a few bats. Occasionally a pipistrelle was seen in early summer; a few were also seen in winter, along with perhaps a dozen wintering little browns.

But on an August evening in 1931 we experienced a virtual bat blitz, easily one hundred bats milling around the cave entrance. So on August 15 we stretched some mosquito netting at the bottom of the throatlike entrance and spent the night here picking off bats as they tried to enter the cave. Among the four species we caught were sixty-five Acadian bats, *Myotis keenii,* a species we almost never found in Pennsylvania at other times of the year.

While we speculated on the unexpected abundance of bats that summer and concluded that some sort of migration was under way, it wasn't until the early 1960s that the widespread occurrence of this late summer phenomenon and its significance were recognized. Reports of this "swarming," as it came to be called, came from the famous Hellhole in West Virginia, from Aitkin Cave in central Pennsylvania, Aeolus Cave in Vermont, Wyandotte Cave in Indiana, and from the most studied site, at Dixon Cave in Mammoth Cave National Park, Kentucky.

83

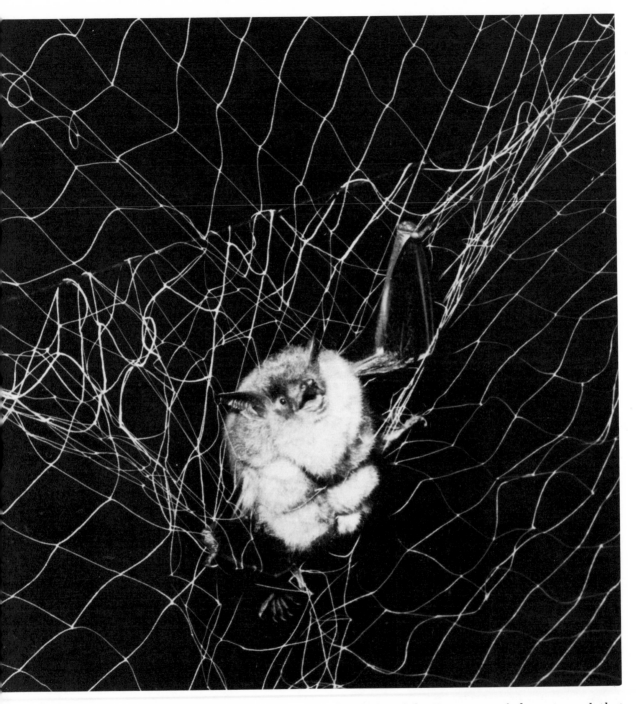

Bats caught in mist nets, when banded and later recaptured, have proved that brief visits during "swarming" are exploratory flights. (Roger W. Barbour)

Autumn

At Dixon Cave, Wayne Davis stretched mist nets of fine nylon filaments over the path beside the large funnel-like entrance and night after night caught hundreds of bats—eight species in all. In banding the captured bats, he discovered that there was almost a complete turnover nightly.

Later, in Canada, M. Brock Fenton of Carleton University, Ottawa, spent more than thirty summer nights at Renfrew Mine, about 50 miles west of Ottawa. The first little brown bats from nursery colonies in barns and other buildings in that region start arriving at the mine as early as July 10, but the swarming flights through the mine do not begin until the end of the month. The first arrivals are males, but by August 1 both sexes—juveniles and adults—are present. On that date in 1967 Fenton caught 263 bats. A year later on the same date 288 were netted. During the 3-year study several banded bats turned up on the same date in different years. It is that regular an occurrence.

The bats certainly were not ready to settle down for the winter. For weeks they are nomads, looking at possible wintering quarters far beyond their accustomed caves. Five of the six longest flights recorded for the swarming Renfrew bats averaged 75 miles; the sixth was 500 miles. The flights appear to be of greatest value to the juveniles, who are "shopping around" for their first winter refuge. The choice is critical because they are less fortified with fat—their winter energy resource—than the more skilled and experienced adults. There is no evidence that juveniles accompany their mothers to their hibernacula, but neither is there proof that they do not.

Migration. In autumn some tree bats follow coastlines on their way to Southern wintering grounds where some insects fly all winter long. Sometimes bats are seen on islands far offshore—at Mount Desert Rock, 30 miles off the coast of Maine, for example, as well as off Cape Cod and Long Island. I have talked with many fishermen who have seen bats flying nearby or alighting on boats off the Delaware and

This hoary bat, Lasiurus cinereus, *hung in a clump of seaside goldenrod during daylight before continuing its flight south.*

New Jersey shores. Evidently many bats take shortcuts, flying over water to distant land projections to the southward, or they may be blown hundreds of miles to sea during storms.

Along the Connecticut shore of Long Island Sound red bats are often seen flying in midafternoon; I have seen groups of four to six red bats there and also along the New Jersey coast. Birdbanders attending mist nets at various "Operation Recovery" stations have caught day-flying bats along with migrating birds.

Off the California coast Richard Tanaza of San Francisco State College observed a migration of hoary bats on South Farallon Island. On this bare rock a single windblown Monterey pine and a grove of cypresses served as a daytime roost for as many as twenty-one bats at a time during an eight-day period from August 30 to September 6, 1965.

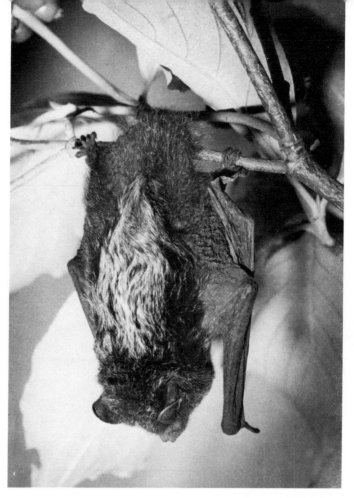

The silver-haired bat, Lasionycteris noctivagans, *is often seen offshore during migration.*

At night, migrants caught aloft in sudden storms may collide with lighthouses, TV towers, and skyscrapers. Birds, unlike bats, have no warning system and probably crash headlong into obstructions. But migrating bats evidently don't depend on sonar for navigation; it is effective only at short distances. Like birds, they too may be whipped back against a structure by air turbulence.

John K. Terres, editor of the *Living World Books,* reported that he found two red bats among 156 birds of eighteen species which struck the Empire State Building in New York City early on the morning of October 19, 1955. A year before, on the night of October 5–6, 1954, hundreds of birds were killed there, along with four red bats. At a lighthouse along Lake Erie A. W. F. Banfield reported a silver-haired bat among many bird storm-victims, and small bands of this species are seen offshore along the New England coast.

87

Cave bats mate in the fall, but fertilization is delayed until hibernation ends.

Mating. Swarming may also be an essential forerunner to mating activity, since it reunites the adult males and females. It is a prenuptial exercise. Pairs of little brown bats are often seen flying in apparent play or courtship. At times one bat is seen pursuing the other at full speed until they are almost together; then they separate for a few seconds—but soon the chase is on again. It may be play, it may be a kind of territorial defense maneuver, if territories are ever claimed by bats. Or it may be courtship prior to copulation. For the little brown bats in the Canadian caves this begins early in September and continues intermittently well into the winter.

During swarming, tree bats are also caught at the caves. Bringing males and females of these solitary bats together results in more than chance encounters. Mating by tree bats is probably no different than among colonial species, but the considerable color difference—bright rufous for males and much duller for females—and the fact that they often fly in the daytime should make it easier for an observer to judge whether any two red bats seen together might be a mating pair.

In 1913 two well-known scientists from the American Museum of Natural History reported that a pair of red bats shot by a collector during an apparent courtship flight in daylight seemed to have been copulating on the wing. Bats do have efficient anatomical arrangements to hold male and female tightly together during copulation. There have been a few additional reports of bats apparently starting to copulate in flight but falling to the ground. Perhaps the availability of night-vision scopes may provide a breakthrough for students of bat behavior.

Return of the Freetails. The long-distance flights that brought the free-tailed bats northward by the tens of millions to nursery caves in the Southwestern states are now reversed. Down from Oklahoma and southern Kansas; down from the great bat caves of the Edwards Plateau in Texas; down from Carlsbad Caverns National Park in New Mexico; down from Eagle Creek Cave in Arizona come the reunited males and females, and the young of the year.

The flights could be disastrous for many of the migrants. Bird-watchers associate weather fronts with large migratory movements of birds, particularly in the fall. Fronts also affect bat migration. At Carlsbad Caverns Constantine kept detailed weather data as part of his study of freetails. During the summer he noted that rainstorms sometimes drenched foraging adults and that currents of cold air reached the bat chamber and could produce a chill factor that could be lethal for rain-soaked bats.

From the first of August until mid-October 1954, Constantine recorded twenty-three cold fronts accompanied by precipitation and lowered temperature and noted buildups of transients from Oklahoma when the storms came from the north. Migrants that failed to find adequate roosting places before dawn were in serious trouble.

Early on the morning of September 17, 1954, he saw unusually large numbers of freetails approaching at great heights from the east.

Most of them eventually found the cave entrance, he reported, but many large groups drifted on westward. At dusk exactly one year earlier he had noticed many large groups coming from the *west*. On that occasion most of them joined the column of freetails leaving the cavern, probably a poor decision for travel-weary bats.

Whether the southward flight from nursery areas is accomplished at a 10,000-foot altitude by freetails, or at treetop level by red bats, or along river systems by some populations of cave bats, the final act is the finding of mates. Copulation follows, but in cave bats, at least, the sperm is stored over winter in the uterus of the female. Ovulation and fertilization will not occur until spring when hibernation comes to an end.

Whether a bat is a hibernator or whether it remains active during the winter after migrating to a warmer climate, a buildup of fat reserves is essential. Fat will be needed to keep the dormant bat alive until spring or to provide energy for a sustained flight of hundreds of miles.

Not all species achieve maximum fat buildup at the same time. The demands of infant rearing followed by the hyperactivity of swarming may account for the fact that female bats have the lowest body weight in late August and early September. Then comes the time for accumulating fat. John Hall found that by early October most Indiana bats have gained 50 percent in weight, the high point of the year. What happens after that is part of the story of hibernation.

Winter

WHERE DO BATS spend the winter? Some, as we have said, particularly the tree bats, fly southward to regions where, presumably, insects can be caught much of the time. That can't be many times a week in Kentucky, where a good many red bats have been seen flying briefly during winter warm spells. Hoary bats are found from time to time in the New York City area, but the migration records we have reported indicate that most of these bats have departed Northern states for the far South. Freetails by the million have gone to Mexico.

The species that hibernate—*Myotis,* for example—have flown as much as 200 to 300 miles to winter in caves and mines. That might seem to account for the whereabouts of most of our bats. Actually, it doesn't.

There is surprising agreement among bat students that only about 15 percent of the bats netted while swarming outside caves—in Ontario, Pennsylvania, and Kentucky—winter in caves. Where do the rest go? Are there important hibernacula still to be discovered? Secret sections in caves that only a bat can reach? Wayne Davis is convinced that one cave in the mountains of Vermont is the hibernaculum of 300,000 bats, but no more than a few thousand have ever been seen in the accessible portions.

Spelunkers are a persistent breed of modern explorers, and they have crawled through 20,000 caves in the United States. Bat experts quickly check on reports of bats being seen, but only a score of sizable new bat roosts have been found in the last twenty years. Most surprising conclusion: Only one cave in fifty makes a good bat cave.

Precise Requirements. Biologists recognize the existence of three life zones in caves: (1) the entrance or twilight zone, where, in Kentucky, for example, winter temperatures may vary thirty degrees, and big browns and least brown bats may hibernate; (2) a more nearly constant zone where temperature fluctuates about five to fifteen degrees, and where most bats hibernate; (3) the innermost zone, an almost constant temperature, 56° in Kentucky, but approximating the *average annual temperature* above ground for the particular *latitude*—lower for higher *altitudes*. Only pipistrelles regularly occupy this warmest zone.

It has gradually become clear that it is not warmth that bats seek in caves, but the lowest stable temperature, short of freezing, that they can find. They are seeking an environment in which the chemi-

Countless Northern caves and mines have virtually constant above-freezing temperatures (except at the entrance) in the 35° to 47° F. range.

cal processes involved in metabolism transform fat into energy at the minimum rate. Not very many caves provide such environmental stability, and conditions that satisfy the needs of one species may be totally unsuitable for a closely related species. This may explain why a few species like *Myotis sodalis* and *M. grisescens* congregate in only about a dozen caves and so are in real peril during the cold half of the year.

The commonest *Myotis,* countrywide, is the little brown bat, *M. lucifugus,* which can be found in moderate numbers in most regions in winter—but so far in none of the 500 caves and mines in Utah visited by John Twente, now of the University of Missouri, who found it a common bat in summer. One of the larger eastern colonies, presently numbering about 6,500, winters in an abandoned iron mine at Hibernia in northern New Jersey. In February and March 1970, John J. McManus of Fairleigh Dickinson University pinpointed the distribution of bats in the tunnellike mine passage, where all bats

The favored roosting section for little browns in Hibernia Mine has a temperature of 35.8° F.

were within easy reach. First he marked off 30-foot sections and recorded the temperature of each. He found a five-degree spread along the innermost 900 feet where the bats were hibernating—34.5° to 39.5° F. Although some bats were seen along the entire hibernating area, 48 percent of them were in the 35.8° F. section, about 1,600 to 1,900 feet into the mine. This precise zone was the optimum for little browns. Bats exposed to higher or lower temperatures, McManus reported, have faster rates of metabolism, use more energy, and accumulate waste products, chiefly urine, more rapidly. This accumulation induces arousal from torpor or dormancy and is followed by flight, urination, and defecation, and drinking from the wet rock surface.

Those bats that settle in the optimum zone do not necessarily possess a finer sense of temperature discrimination. It is just that the ones that hang up where the air and the rock surface are 35.8° F. will arouse only at long intervals. McManus found that 90 percent of the bats in the warmest area, 39.5° F., changed position within an average of 4.5 days. Even on the basis of chance they would soon find a more favorable—that is, cooler—spot.

In Carter Caves State Park in northeastern Kentucky, Wayne Davis and his students found *M. lucifugus* only in the outer, colder part of Bat Cave, which averaged about 36° F. But the 100,000 *M. sodalis* were concentrated in interconnecting rooms a thousand feet farther into the cave, where it was a bit warmer, from 37° to 43° F. Davis often found dozens of active, squeaking *M. sodalis* in one still-warmer area—54° to 57° F.—and in October he observed copulating bats by the hundreds there.

Whereas little browns hang in small, fairly loose clusters, the Indiana bats form a tapestry that reveals only faces and elbows. Equally large aggregations are formed by gray bats, but in slightly warmer situations—45° to 50° F. This may account for their hibernating pos-

Access to this huge colony of Indiana bats, Myotis sodalis, *in Bat Cave in Carter Caves State Park, Kentucky, is barred during the hibernating season.*

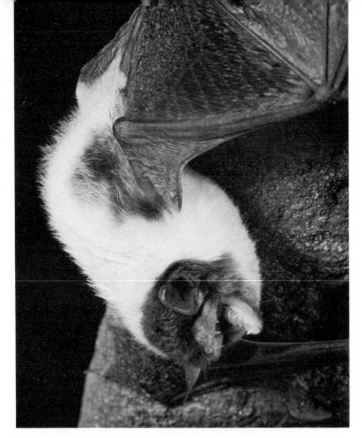

One partly white individual was found among 100,000 Indiana bats. (Roger W. Barbour)

A 6-inch-square frame aids in a count of these Indiana bats in a Kentucky cave.

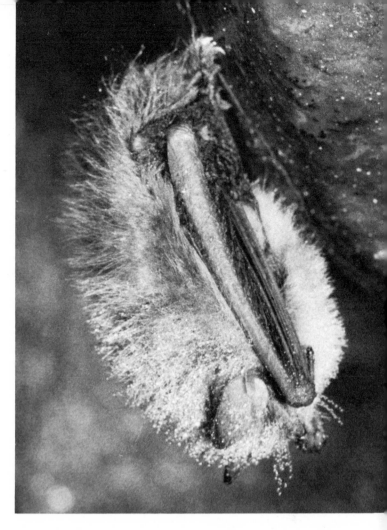

Dew condensed on this pipistrelle, Pipistrellus subflavus, *where relative humidity measured 99° F.*

ture—less crowded, since their forearms stick out so much that a cluster appears interwoven.

The specific site chosen by each species also involves humidity. The air in many cave and mine passages seems dry; explorers often kick up dust but a psychrometer generally records at least 85 percent relative humidity—97 to 100 percent at bat roosts. Little browns and pipistrelles are often covered with droplets of moisture and appear to choose areas where the humidity measures 99 percent.

Bats don't go directly to the sections of the cave where we find them in midwinter. The move to the main hibernating site is a gradual one unless the entrance is too large to protect the bats against extremely low temperatures in early winter. Griffin found 800 little browns in a cave in Vermont in November and December, but only 50 in February.

97

Some remained as corpses frozen into icicles, part of columns of ice filling passages where bats were roosting earlier. Many of the abandoned mines I have visited in Connecticut and Massachusetts have a number of entrances, letting in enough subfreezing air to make them inhospitable for would-be hibernators.

If a healthy little brown bat finds a favorable environment for hibernation—with no disturbance—it can survive a long winter. At optimum temperature of 36° F. it would expend energy at the rate of twenty calories per day, a total of 3,000 calories of energy for an average 150-day period of hibernation.

The metabolic energy yield of 1 gram of fat is 9,500 calories. Since most individual bats burn up 2 grams during the winter, it is apparent that much of the time the bat's metabolism rises far above the state of complete dormancy. If it didn't, a bat could theoretically survive at that level for six years. It doesn't have to do that, but its whole life-style is so regulated—its lifetime energy use so budgeted— that it far outlives similar-sized insectivores, the shrews. A tiny shrew, with its furious living pace, may expend as many calories in a sixteen-month life span as a little brown bat does in twenty years. And a good many little browns have survived that long or longer.

For little brown bats, buildings just aren't suitable for hibernation, especially heated ones. Even in unheated structures these bats would experience too much fluctuation from the optimum temperature at which the consumption of stored fat proceeds most slowly.

Buildings have doubtless provided roosts that have benefited many bats, but they don't provide long-term security—nor do caves, for that matter. Humphrey reports a 52 percent loss of little brown nursery sites in Indiana in a decade and a staggering 80 percent loss in wintering populations.

Natural Disasters. Even where the cave environment is ideal, hazards may still exist. When I made my first trip of the winter to central

This black rat snake reached the roof of the cave, caught a hibernating Indiana bat, constricted it, and swallowed it head first. (Thomas C. Barr, Jr.)

In 1950 this canyon swiftly filled with water that rose to the ceiling, nearly trapping bat expert Donald Griffin and his party and drowning most of the bats.

Twenty years after the flood a few hundred little brown bats winter here.

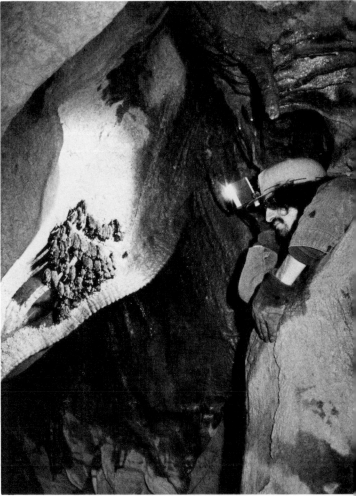

Winter

Pennsylvania's leading hibernaculum—Aitkin Cave—in early December 1950, I knew that its 5,000 or so little browns should be deeply dormant but that its few least brown bats and big browns had probably just arrived. I was in for a surprise. There were no big clusters. Hardly a live bat could be found. Here and there in a crevice there were dead bats, and a few hanging from formations had mold growing on them. Scores of dead bats were scattered over the slippery mud banks. In one of the higher chambers I found some equipment that I knew Donald Griffin had used to record bat calls during trips from Cornell University 180 miles to the north.

A week later I received a lengthy letter from Griffin describing the "deluge underground" he and his party had experienced Thanksgiving weekend. While they were camping in the rain near the cave, their tents were nearly washed away by rising flood waters. Inside the cave, the water rose so fast that the party barely escaped. Here and there I found small clusters of live bats, chiefly in the highest places, where air might have been trapped above the flood waters. It can only be guessed how many bats perished in the flooded cave, since most of the carcasses must have been carried away by the receding water.

There was no bone deposit here, but in a small cave 90 feet above the Green River in Mammoth Cave National Park, I saw bushels of bones. My guide had led John Hall to this same cave ten years earlier, but it still took us a couple of hours to find it. Hall had found the bones of more Indiana bats in this cave than are known today in all the bat caves in the park. The bone deposit measured 3 feet wide and about 20 feet long and averaged 7 or 8 inches deep—300,000 bats had died here! The skulls—and the bushels of bones that looked like pine needles on a forest floor—were the remains of flood victims, possibly of the record floods of 1937. This bone deposit is one of the best answers to the question, "Why should an animal such as the Indiana bat, whose present population may number half a million, be classified as endangered?"

Spring floods carry leaves and decaying wood into caves, providing an energy source for cave dwellers.

Mold grows on damp wood, also on animal excrement.

Indiana bats from six or seven states in the Ohio-Mississippi drainage converge on a dozen caves each fall. Many of the caves are protected—Mammoth Cave, Carter Caves, and Wyandotte Cave—but no one can predict how safe they are from catastrophic floods.

Inside the Caves. Little is happening to the hibernating bats. Most individuals will have moved back from exposed entrances. Metabolic use of stored fat is increased briefly when it is necessary to raise body temperatures above freezing or to relocate to a more favorable environment. But such moves are infrequent.

Some species actually prefer caves where the temperature barely exceeds freezing. Oddly enough, this is particularly true of the largest and the smallest of eastern bats that hibernate—the big brown, *Eptesi-*

103

cus fuscus, and the least brown, *Myotis leibii.* In addition to picking a spot very close to the entrance, they are the last to begin hibernation. In some mild winters few big browns come into the caves at all. In severe winters I have seen a hundred or more jammed into a crack 2 inches wide within 30 feet of the entrance of a Pennsylvania cave. In Minnesota an early snowstorm in November 1940 blocked a cave entrance with drifts, and over 100 big browns died trying to enter.

Bats in the Tropics. In the extreme Southern United States most bats are active the year round. Flower bats, of course, migrate back into Mexico, where certain species of flowers bloom during the winter. Much is known about the travels of cave bats, but comparatively little about the winter habits and behavior of non-cave-dwelling, non-insectivorous bats. In recent years many mammalogists have gone to tropical and semitropical areas, where far more species of bats exist than in the temperate zones.

Even a brief brush with tropical species can be exciting, as I learned while spending three weeks with an Explorers Club expedition in Guatemala in the winter of 1968. The purpose of the trip, which was filmed for ABC, was to solve the "Riddle of the Mayan Cave"—to discover why Mayan Indians visited certain caves over a period of 2,000 years. Lifelong friends Russell and Jeanne Gurnee headed the expedition, and Brother Nicholas Sullivan and I went along as biologists to make a quick survey of cave life while the archaeologists and geologists carried on other investigations. Naturally, bats were high on my list of concerns. We found four types: insect eaters, fruit eaters, nectar drinkers, and the infamous vampire bat, which lives exclusively on blood.

Just inside Lanquin Cave, a Guatemalan National Park, we discovered a roost of small bats, about 2,000, hanging from the ceiling. Ricelike pellets of guano covered the floor, identifying the bats as insect eaters. Emerging from the cave about half an hour before dark,

The big brown bat, Eptesicus, and the least brown bat, Myotis leibii, *choose the coldest hibernating spots, barely above freezing.*

The least brown bat is one of the smallest in the United States.

This tropical naked-backed bat, an insect eater, flew into the expedition's laboratory and hung up on the bottle containing the same species!

the bats flew back and forth only inches above the swift-flowing river which also came from inside the cave. Individual bats took a break from time to time, perching in the branches of overhanging trees. I managed to snatch a couple by crawling up a sloping tree trunk. They were members of a tiny species, *Pteronotus daveyi,* known as "naked-backed" bats because their wing membranes meet along the midline of the back, giving them the appearance of being hairless from shoulder to tail.

Back in the cave the next day, crawling around on hands and knees in search of beetles, millipedes, spiders, and other small creatures, we were pelted with marble-sized green seeds or hard fruit accidentally dropped by the bats. We had already noticed low mounds composed of dozens—sometimes scores—of these objects. Other, smaller seeds had passed through the bats' digestive systems. Ghostly forests grew from the seeds, reaching a height of 10 to 20 inches. Most of the plants had a pair of seed leaves, and the stems were tinged with red or brown—no green, of course, because in the absence of light no chlorophyll could develop, and growth stopped as soon as the energy stored in each seed was used up.

Our flashlights pinpointed several large bats on the ceiling above us, and occasional fruit fragments, like fine wood shavings, came drifting down to fall amid the sprouting seeds. Almost everywhere that we found bats we also found small accumulations of sprouting seeds.

During the five days we spent in Lanquin Cave we captured nine species of bats, including fierce-looking *Sturnira*, with a wingspan of 17 inches. Like many other tropical bats, it has a big "nose-leaf," a

Seeds dropped by fruit bats sprout and grow until their stored energy is used up. (Self-portrait by the author)

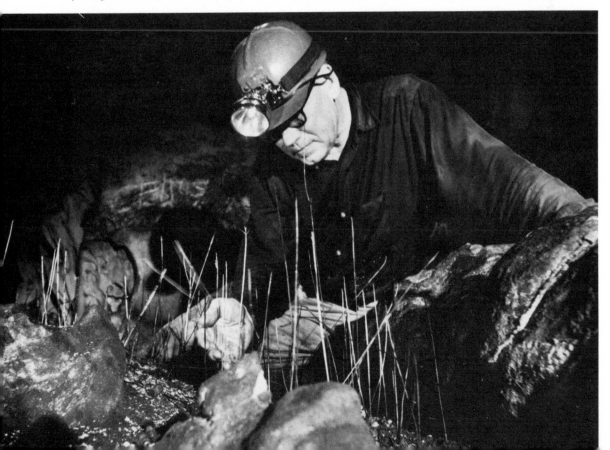

spearlike protuberance which may help to drain moisture off the bat's face as it hangs downward.

A Trap for Vampires. I had been hoping all along to capture a vampire bat, without luck. Now our two dozen horses and burros might attract vampire bats. We stretched a 30-foot mist net in the middle of the corral and bedded down early. When I made the first inspection around 9 P.M., I found two bats struggling in the net. Their flat faces and huge thumbs identified them—vampires! By the time the camera crew had been awakened two more bats were entangled: a fruit bat, *Artibeus,* and a long-nosed variety, *Glossophaga.*

Brother Nick and I wore heavy leather gloves while positioning the vampires in front of the cameras. When the filming was over I removed my cumbersome gloves to take a few flash shots. Finished with that, I decided to collect the specimens, realizing that they would chew their way out of the net before morning. The fruit bat was easy. Then I snipped the net around a vampire and pulled the collecting bag up around it. Just as I pressed the bag shut, I felt a stab in my right hand. The vampire's projecting incisors had slashed through the bag's thick plastic and into my palm, removing a small bit of flesh.

Our physician washed and bandaged the wound—barely an eighth of an inch wide and half as deep, but enough to kill if the bat happened to be rabid. It wouldn't have been so urgent if I had been vaccinated for rabies before the trip, but I hadn't planned to give any bat a chance to bite me. Fortunately, I had the culprit—the bat that bit me—and the next morning I could take it to Guatemala City to be tested for rabies. If the test was positive, I could get the vaccination shots, a painful but lifesaving experience.

The plastic bag containing the vampire lay on the ground beside my sleeping bag throughout the night. Several times I could hear it flopping around—a reassuring sound, since I needed to get it to the laboratory alive. I rose at intervals to check the net in the clearing.

There were more bats entangled in it, of the varieties we had already collected. Other smaller bats wheeled about the clearing but, being insect eaters with excellent sonar, they avoided the net. Other, larger bats, almost certainly vampires, circled low over the horses and mules. In the morning we discovered that one horse had a fresh wound on its shoulder.

Morning brought another, grimmer discovery: Army ants had discovered the vampire and had cut their way through the thick plastic. Thousands of them were inside the bag, consuming the bat. I desperately began removing the ants from the bat's body. The task completed, I saw with relief that the head was intact. It was the brain tissue that was needed for the test. Even though the bat was dead, it would be possible to do the test if we got the bat to the laboratory quickly. After driving the Land Rover over 40 miles of mountainous roads in a record three hours, we reached the airfield with minutes to spare. An hour later my plane landed in Guatemala City, and I rushed to the laboratory, which had been alerted by radio. I had made it in time; the results would be available in twenty-four hours.

Exactly twenty-four hours later, Dr. Herbert Quirin handed me the negative report and assured me that, despite the delay, the result was quite reliable. However, as a final safeguard he was proceeding with a second test. "The suspected animal does not bite with its brain," he told me. There had been cases when the test for Negri bodies—the indicators of rabies in brain tissue—had been negative, but when tissue from the salivary glands was injected into newborn mice the mice died from rabies. If the bat that bit me was rabid, the mice would be dead in time to start my series of twenty-one inoculations. Happily, the mice did not die.

Into a Vampire Cave. My enforced return to Guatemala City gave me an opportunity to visit a vampire bat roost. Director Jorge A. Ibarra of the National Museum of Guatemala led me to a horizontal shaft

109

that had been drilled in search of water. Unsuccessful and dry, it had been occupied by a small colony of vampires. Since no livestock on nearby farms had developed rabies, the bats were not molested.

The entranceway and the first 15 feet had to be negotiated by crawling, and after that it was possible to crouch and then to walk upright, although the passage was barely 2 feet wide. There was the distinctive odor of vampires, a sickly sweet smell I had noticed in vampire caves in Mexico. Vampires hung from the wall just ahead. Some, disturbed by our entrance, launched themselves with powerful leg thrusts and disappeared down the passage. Others scrambled about the walls as agilely as crabs or spiders, seemingly reluctant to fly. Still others appeared too young to take wing, but jumped to the floor of the shaft and bounded ahead of us, looking for all the world like toads. They hopped faster than we could follow or disappeared into passages too small for us to enter.

Finally, our way was blocked by a second wall-to-wall pool of reddish-black, tarlike excrement. Soon after they reenter the cave after a night out dining, the vampires void excess portions of their meal of blood. Its presence in a cave is unmistakable evidence of vampire bats. We turned back, stopping only long enough to collect a pint of the excrement and a sampling of the insects and other invertebrates that inhabit the viscous mess.

Back at the National Museum I examined skulls of all three species of vampires, the abundant *Desmodus* and the rare *Diphylla* and *Diaemus*. All live exclusively on blood; the latter two, however, seem to prefer to get their meals from birds, though *Diaemus* also preys on small domestic mammals. *Diaemus* is of interest in other ways. It possesses unique buccal (cheek) glands that give off a foul odor of undetermined use. The hairy-legged vampire, as it is called, is the only living vampire bat that has been taken in the United States. One specimen that strayed far north of its normal Mexican limits was taken in a railroad tunnel 12 miles west of Comstock, Texas, in 1968.

A vampire walks on thumbs and folded wings and bites with incisors and canines. (Courtesy Nicandro Gomez, USIS, U.S. Embassy, Mexico City)

Fossilized skulls of *Desmodus* have been found in cave deposits in Florida and California, associated with other extinct animals that lived in warmer Pleistocene times when the minimum winter temperature was above the 40° F. level that limits the present distribution of *Desmodus*.

The skull of *Desmodus* is notable for the reduced number of teeth and their specialization for bloodletting. The projecting upper incisors slice out a bit of flesh, as I have already noted. Even more wicked looking are the upper canines, whose function was a mystery until longtime vampire specialist Arthur M. Greenhall reported in 1972 that the inner surface of these "eye teeth" is beveled, producing a concave shaving surface which, when the head is swung sideways, can evidently remove hairs from the hide of the prey animal and then remove layers of skin until the blood begins to flow. The presence of a depilatory agent in the saliva is suspected, but unproved. The vampire's known ability to inflict a painless bite on a sleeping victim requires that sharpness of the cutting surface be maintained. Greenhall reports frequent jaw action that slides cutting surfaces against each other in a possible self-sharpening action.

How much blood is taken? As many as ten one-ounce vampires may feed on one animal each night, consuming their own weight in blood every twenty-four hours, but the victim may lose double that amount because of an anticlotting agent in the vampire's saliva—something suspected since 1932 but not identified until 1966. In livestock the actual blood loss from nightly feeding may be rated as serious—possibly 1.5 liters—but the exposure of the victim's wounds to infection and, in some areas, to transmission of rabies virus creates a major economic problem throughout Latin America, a topic discussed in the next chapter.

Other Cave Dwellers. While looking into every cave I heard about as I continued searching for bats, I encountered a variety of tiny cave dwellers. The greatest number and variety always seemed to live in bat caves. That isn't surprising, because directly or indirectly their existence there is dependent on an abundant food source—guano. In some caves, too small to serve as bat roosts, cricket guano provides the basic energy source for populations of cave animals.

The temperature and light zonation which affects the distribution of bats in caves can also be recognized by the presence of distinctive communities of plants and animals. Green plants can grow only in the twilight zone, and temperature fluctuations there force the spiders and snails, eyed salamanders, frogs, flatworms, amphipods, and isopods to move many times to stay in a tolerable environment—but these sites are still spared the extremes of temperature and moisture found above ground. Based on their degree of adaptation to cave conditions, most of these creatures I have mentioned, along with bats, would be classed as *trogloxenes*—cave guests—animals which regularly enter

The pack rat goes out at night to gather food, nesting materials, and trophies.

This salamander lives in the variable-temperature, dimly lighted entrance zone.

Cave cricket guano feeds smaller cave creatures where bat guano is not available.

caves but must return periodically to the surface. Cold-blooded animals such as frogs and surface fishes might survive for years if trapped in a cave, but they cannot reproduce there.

A few species of eyed fish seem preadapted to cave conditions through life in dark habitats. They are *troglophiles*—cave lovers—able to complete their life cycles either in caves or above ground. This category includes some eyed crayfish and salamanders, certain cave crickets and spiders—animal life familiar in rural cellarways and other similar habitats.

Certain white, frequently eyeless, creatures are unique to caves and subterranean waters. They are obliged by their modified anatomy and behavior to live in the unvarying environment of the deep and usually extensive underground cave systems found south of the front of the continental glaciers of the last Ice Age. Called *troglobites*—cave dwellers—they include blind fish and salamanders, white crayfish, eyeless flatworms, amphipods, isopods, and spiders, as well as pigmented but blind beetles and other terrestrial invertebrates.

114

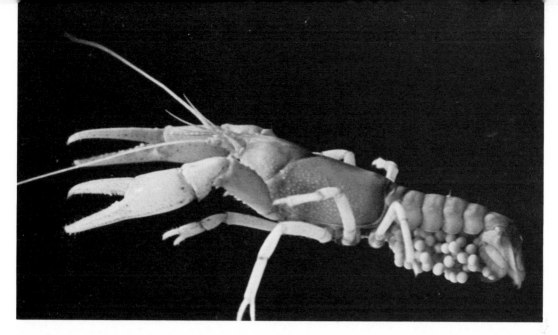

The blind white crayfish is a true cave dweller, a troglobite. The female carries her eggs until they hatch.

Cave flatworms live in a "soup" of bat guano in an Oklahoma cave.

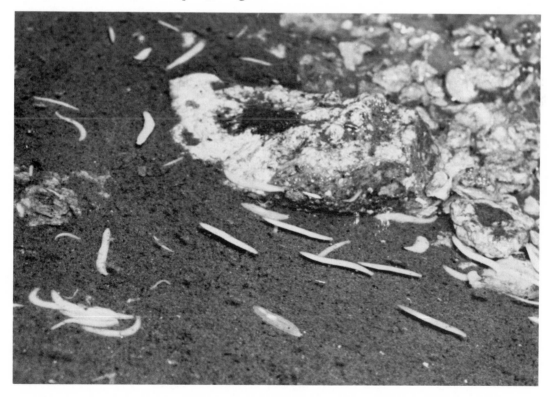

This rare Texas cave isopod swims close to a bat skull—searching for a shred of flesh?

An Ozark blind cave salamander approaches a pile of bones of dead tree bats, doomed when they roosted, became dormant, and were unable to arouse and fly from the cave.

Blind cave beetles in Kentucky find an unusual food source—a dead gray bat.

The greatest variety of troglobites have been found in Mammoth Cave with its more than 150 miles of surveyed passageways. Another area of abundant cave life is found in the Ozark Mountains of Missouri, Arkansas, and eastern Oklahoma. Northern Florida and much of Tennessee and Kentucky also lie in areas of deeply bedded, cavernous limestone, and in all these regions bat populations are concentrated in caves. In the Southwest, few big bat caves contain streams, so the bulk of troglobites, the aquatic forms, are absent. But terrestrial cave dwellers, though tiny, may be incredibly abundant and bothersome, as the bats, and the students of bats, have discovered.

Thousands of bats find shelter in gated caves within 50,000-acre Mammoth Cave National Park, Kentucky. Many more swarm here as transients.

Bats and Man

POSSIBLY NO WELL-KNOWN animal was as little appreciated and understood in the past as was the bat. None has suffered as much from superstition and fear. Yet today, largely through the news media—TV, newspapers, periodicals, and books—the public has almost overnight discovered that bats are fascinating rather than loathsome; that they are valuable members of natural ecosystems, not enemies; and that some of them are seriously threatened by man's activities.

Metabolic economy is doubtless the key to the survival of bats, particularly during the winter. Anything that stimulates the bat to arousal is likely to cause a marked increase in the metabolism and the rate of fat utilization. The result is a shortening of the time over which the bat can survive without finding a dependable source of food.

Too many biological investigators have recognized the fact that bats alone, among hibernating animals, can be found with certainty, observed at close range under natural conditions for extended periods of time and found year after year, and so have disturbed bat populations repeatedly. Many bats have been sacrificed in experiments of doubtful value.

As early as 1953, I reported alarming decreases in bat colonies in the Northeast. By 1970 the disturbance of hibernating bats by researchers and cave explorers had reached a critical point in many of

119

the more accessible cave areas. Some species, particularly *Myotis sodalis,* the Indiana bat, and the big-eared *Plecotus,* seem very easily disturbed. Northeastern populations of *sodalis* have vanished from all established hibernacula; it is unlikely that they have merely moved to alternative quarters.

Other species, such as the familiar little brown bat, are more tolerant, not easily disturbed. In the fall of 1972 residents around Hibernia, New Jersey, about 100 miles west of New York City, were alarmed when scores of houses were invaded by little brown bats. It had never happened before, although most bat students knew that the abandoned iron mine at Hibernia was the winter refuge for thousands of little browns. This is where John McManus determined that the bats sought a temperature of 35.8° F. for their winterlong hibernation.

The mine was sold in 1972, and the new owners closed all known air shafts. Bats accustomed to reaching their wintering locations by those entrances went scouting for new quarters. Happily, most of them eventually found access to the mine through unsealed shafts. The near panic among people lasted for a couple of weeks, but the crisis in the lives of the little brown bats seems to have been resolved, at least for this particular population. Many other environmental changes, however, are under way, countrywide and worldwide. The effect of various disturbances is hard to evaluate.

Dams. In June 1932 I went looking for gray bats in Nickajack Cave, which lies close to the junction of Tennessee, Georgia, and Alabama; I had found the first Indiana bats for the region there the previous winter. In December I had stripped and waded chin deep in the underground river to reach the far bank and the hibernating bats when the rowboat I had counted on using proved to be completely unseaworthy. In June I didn't need to cross the stream—the gray bats hung in clusters over the near bank, all too accessible in a cave that

Partially flooded in 1968 by a TVA dam, Nickajack Cave now provides more security for its wintering Indiana bats and a nursery colony of gray bats.

was a popular place for picnic parties. Now, however, a giant new TVA dam backs water partially up into the awesome entrance. This has put a stop to forays by picnickers while still leaving the bats adequate room for nursery and hibernation sites. And in summer foraging is fine over the lake.

It is possible that the series of dams planned for the cave-dotted Meramec Valley in Missouri may have similar trade-off benefits for gray bats which occupy certain caves there. Greater protection from disturbance may be afforded the bats by partially flooding nursery refuge entrances. But the flooding of these cave ecosystems may indeed represent ecological disasters. Fortunately, comprehensive studies of

121

Bats such as these Plecotus townsendii *in Jewel Cave National Monument, South Dakota, benefit from the protection provided by the Park Service.*

the specific caves and their populations of possibly unique cave animals have been undertaken to provide data for a competent judgment of the environmental impact of such dam building.

Conservation Efforts. Creation of the Office of Endangered Species in the U.S. Fish and Wildlife Service gives promise of effective enforcement of new Federal regulations such as the banning of Federal funding for projects which would have harmful effects on endangered species of wildlife.

Bat specialists have cooperated fully in helping in the preparation of detailed "recovery plans" for endangered species, such as one for the Indiana bat, developed by the U.S. Fish and Wildlife Service. A similar plan is being developed for the newest addition to the United States List of Endangered Species—the gray bat, *Myotis grisescens.* There is encouraging evidence that the strong public acceptance of such regulatory measures and recovery plans has helped improve the image of bats of all species.

Similar steps are being taken by state agencies. Organizations such as the American Society of Mammalogists and the National Speleological Society have acted to protect threatened and endangered species from disturbances by biologists and spelunkers. Unwarranted use of bats in poorly conceived experiments is being effectively curtailed.

Key caves and mines need to be acquired and protected by government agencies or private groups such as the Nature Conservancy and cooperating organizations such as the National Audubon Society. This would be only fair, since large numbers of bats have perished as a result of man's activities, some in truly inhumane schemes. I sometimes wonder how many million *Tadarida* died while they were being prepared for a secret military operation during World War II.

Project X-Ray. The team selected for this top secret project included a college student, Denny G. Constantine, who years later became the chief bat investigator for the U.S. Public Health Service. It was headed by a resourceful Pennsylvania surgeon-inventor, Lyle Adams. I talked with him shortly after the disclosure of what has been described as one of the most extraordinary military operations ever conceived. "On December 7, 1941, I was driving near Washington when I heard the news of the attack on Pearl Harbor," Adams told me. "How could we fight back? Our Navy was crippled. What offensive weapons could we use?"

Adams had seen the bat flight at Carlsbad Caverns the previous summer and now conceived the idea of fitting bats with incendiary bombs and dropping them from planes over Japanese industrial centers, fleet concentrations, ammunition dumps, and underground storage depots. The bats would seek shelter in cracks and crevices and set off a multitude of explosions and fires. Top military officials listened to his proposal and authorized it. While Adams led a search for bat colonies, scientists experimented with firebombs small enough for a bat to carry. After several species were tried, the abundant freetail, *Tadarida brasiliensis,* was selected, and vast numbers were captured at Ney and Bracken Caves in Texas and kept in a dormant state in mammoth freezers. Bomb-shaped containers resembling giant egg crates holding up to 5,000 bats were prepared. A one-ounce time bomb was designed and manufactured and attached to the loose skin over the bat's chest by a surgical clip and a short length of string. When the small bomb ignited, it produced a 22-inch flame which burned with intense heat for eight minutes, quite sufficient to set almost anything afire. The bats were expendable.

Shortly after I talked with Adams, Constantine visited me at the Academy of Natural Sciences in Philadelphia and described other details of the project. Efforts to preserve secrecy were not successful, he said. Heavy traffic by military trucks was not unusual, but when certain vehicles stopped, the squeaking of thousands of unseen bats inside attracted lots of attention and much speculation. When bats carrying unarmed bombs escaped from the experimental area and were discovered roosting beneath a municipal gas tank, there was considerable public alarm, even though at the time it was not generally known that dummy houses constructed throughout a 1,250-square-mile desert area had burned in a practice bombing or that a couple of bats with live bombs had escaped and had set fire to several buildings at the project headquarters. Throughout the several years of development, Constantine said, it was generally thought that Project X-Ray would not be used because it might be classed as a biological weapon, even though no microbiological agents were involved. Nevertheless, members of the project were stunned and mystified by the stop-work order in October 1944. No reason was given, but without doubt the order came from high officials who knew that another and more deadly weapon, also tested in the Southwestern desert, would soon be ready.

Vampire Bat Control. Twenty years after Project X-Ray was suddenly terminated, another bomb-carrying mission was considered—equipping captured vampire bats with explosive or gas bombs and releasing them to fly back and destroy their own roost and its vampire population.

The project was never implemented, but it reflects the desperation and the futility of thirty-five years' effort to protect Latin American livestock from rabies-carrying vampire bats. Following World War II, chemical warfare and demolition experts, particularly in Trinidad, Mexico, Venezuela, and Brazil, attacked bat roosts with a ferocity that appalled naturalists and other ecologists. Poison gas, flamethrowers, explosives, and electrocution exterminated bats in 8,240 caves in Brazil, while 900,000 bats of many species in Venezuela were killed annually during a three-year-long campaign in the mid-1960s.

Livestock losses in Mexico had reached 100,000 a year; in Latin America, 1,000,000, valued at $250,000,000. In addition, thousands of

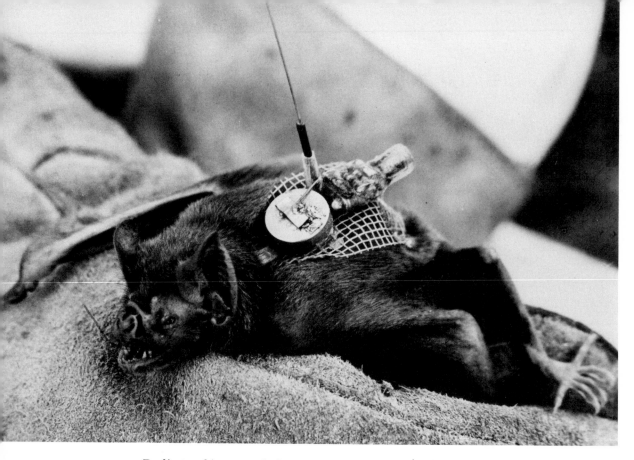

Radio tracking revealed roosts of vampires. (Richard J. Burns, Colorado Research Center)

horses died in 1970–71 from equine encephalitis, caused by a virus believed carried by vampire bats as well as by birds.

A major counterattack on the vampire bat got under way in 1968 when the U.S. Agency for International Development (AID), in cooperation with the Mexican Government, assigned to the Fish and Wildlife Service the job of developing an ecologically sound control program. Using sophisticated surveillance equipment such as miniaturized radio transmitters on bats and night-vision scopes borrowed from the U.S. Army, researchers watched the bats feed on livestock, something they did only in the absence of moonlight. Intensive, unsuspected grooming of the vampires and their neighbors in their crowded roosts was observed with closed-circuit television, under red light illumination.

The grooming habit supplied the researchers with a solution. With a slow-acting, poison-bearing paste containing an anticoagulant, paint the ankle, fetlock, shoulder, or neck where a cow has been bitten. The bat will be back and will get smeared with the jellylike toxicant. At the roost again, it cleans itself by licking and spreads a good deal on its neighbors for them to clean off. In three days enough is consumed to wipe out the vampire colony. Other species are unaffected.

Where trained workers are available, they catch vampires in mist nets close to the livestock and smear them liberally with the deadly paste. On big cattle ranches veterinarians now routinely give a shot of the anticoagulant directly into the rumen, one of the four stomach compartments of cattle.

The small amount circulated in the bloodstream doesn't harm the cow or its milk but is sufficient to cause internal bleeding—as similar poisons do in rats—in the heavy-drinking vampire bat, which consumes at least its own weight in blood each night.

The anticoagulant is being used successfully in Mexico but even more dramatically in Central and South America, with mortality in some of the most bothersome vampire roosts running between 90 and 95 percent. During a seventeen-month period in 1974–75 a total of 78,500 cattle were treated in Nicaragua, and thirty days later vampire bites had been reduced by 91 percent. Vampire bites of humans, which had reached 300 annually in Nicaragua, declined in the same degree.

With a few notable exceptions, the discoveries about vampire bat behavior and ecology in recent years have been spin-offs of the AID control programs begun in 1968. In 1972 Dennis C. Turner, a Johns Hopkins University doctoral student working under Edwin Gould, undertook a fifteen-month investigation in Guatemala which William Wimsatt describes as "without doubt the most broadly conceived, rigorous and carefully controlled study of natural behavioral patterns of vampires and their objective analysis that has yet appeared." Turner's book, *The Vampire Bat,* published in 1975, reports and analyzes much new data.

127

Among other things, Turner presents evidence that bats establish and defend territory—in this case a particular cow or herd—and that resident bats probably recognize members of their own roost group, perhaps by the odor of vampire urine on the cow, and may drive off transient vampires. The new study should be fascinating to a wide spectrum of biologists, especially to the scientists responsible for the veterinary strategy designed to control the costly vampire predation on livestock.

Sophisticated Sonar. The Navy uses echo detectors—sonar—to locate submarines, schools of fish, and seamounts. The Air Force relies on radar to detect unseen aircraft or to determine distance to the surface or to aerial targets. Military interest in the bat's ability to direct a burst of sound and hear the echo from a target as tiny as a fruit fly, recognize it, correct course as the target moves erratically, and intercept it—all within half a second—springs from the likelihood that bats possess echolocation refinements not possessed by the first electronic devices or even those of today.

Since early in World War II, Armed Forces contracts have supported research on bats, such as the studies carried on by Griffin. The timely invention of the high-speed electronic flash by Harold E. Edgerton at the Massachusetts Institute of Technology made it possible to freeze on film the unsuspected, intricate maneuvers involved in the bat's catching a flying insect. Seeking clues to overcome radar jamming, scientists studied a bat's ability to distinguish obstacle from insect target and to select faint but essential echoes from among loud blasts of sound.

Airport Hazard. It is a well-known fact that large flights of migratory birds such as swallows and blackbirds, and flocks of gulls around coastal or lakefront airports, have interfered with planes landing or taking off during the day. In much the same way, bats can be hazardous to low-flying planes at night—one in nine flights at Randolph Air Force Base, Texas, in August, experienced strikes. This field is about 10 miles from Bracken Cave, a roost for one of the world's largest known bat colonies—about 20 million freetails. Although they may not emerge from the cave until after dusk, their presence can be detected on a radar screen. Timothy Williams and his wife, Janet, repeatedly watched swarms of bats follow a narrow path as they emerged and ranged up to 10,000 feet. Then the flight spread into a diffuse ring, which soon expanded to 15 to 20 miles in diameter. Presence of the radar-detected bats was confirmed by the Williamses from a helicopter equipped with floodlights—bats flashed through the beam faster than they could be counted. Earlier, at dusk, the bats were watched as the emerging column first broke into large groups of up to 10,000 animals, then into groups of about 1,000, finally into flocks of about 100—and disappeared at speeds up to 60 mph. The study provided no alternative to the daily bat-traffic alert to approaching pilots.

Fortunately, few airports must cope with a bat menace. Military interest stems much more from the bat's surprisingly sophisticated, ultra-miniature echolocation system.

Aid for the Blind. There are, however, more humanitarian applications of bat research. Griffin has long believed that better understanding of a bat's use of echolocation might be of inestimable help in increasing a blind person's limited ability to detect certain obstacles in time to avoid colliding with them. Experiments at Cornell University in the 1940s proved that this skill, possessed in varying degrees by humans, definitely depends on echolocation. Blind persons whose ears are plugged become as confused as those bats deafened by Spallanzani and Jurine in the 1790s or by Griffin when he repeated and expanded those classic experiments in the late 1930s. Sonar-type electronic devices now on the market function as an adjunct to a cane or guide dog, but new advances promise devices which will let their sightless users "see" their surroundings well enough to walk confidently.

In 1975 Tom Bowers, at Stanford University, fitted a blind infant with a sonic headgear that transmits sound pulses forward for 6 feet within an 80-degree cone and converts the echoes into audible signals fed into each ear. Like a bat, the child as he moves about perceives variations in pitch and intensity associated with the size, surface, and distance of the target.

Organic Fertilizer. Animal manure has been a reliable source of agricultural fertilizer almost as long as man has been cultivating crops. Before Carlsbad Caverns was set aside as a National Park, half a million dollars' worth of nitrogen-rich guano had been mined there and sold. Most of the big Texas bat caves were also mined during and after the Civil War. Even caves difficult of access in the walls of the Grand

This Mammoth Cave visitor center display shows how cave earth was treated in leaching vats as early as 1812 to obtain nitrates for gunpowder.

Canyon in Arizona have been mined and the guano carried out by aerial tramway.

Proof of Air Pollution. Mining operators knew of Eagle Creek Cave and its vast bat guano deposits long before biologists did. It was completely cleaned out in the spring of 1954. J. Scott Altenbach, of Colorado State University, discovered that annual guano layers could be recognized. It occurred to him that they might be as revealing of atmospheric and other events as are the annual growth rings in trees. Assisted by Michael Petit, he drove a stovepipe to the bottom of the deepest guano deposit. Back at the laboratory they cut a strip from top to bottom and looked at the series of seventeen annual layers. Some mercury from copper ore was found in each layer, but the amount was least in annual layers associated with shutdowns of the huge Phelps-Dodge open-pit copper mine and smelters located just 8 miles from Eagle Creek Cave.

Extensive blasting produces particles that may be carried by air currents, along with fumes or minute particles from the huge smelters, and some of the particles are carried into the cave and settle in the guano. There is also evidence, however, that the mercury from the copper ore was being ingested by the bats when they ate mercury-bearing insects.

In light of the fantastic number of insects that bats eat, the mercury buildup from concentration in insect flesh and juices may be serious for the bats. Altenbach and Petit found measurable amounts in the guano but have yet to determine at what point—or over what length of time—the doses of mercury might result in the bat's death. This newly recognized hazard, added to the widespread exposure of freetails to pesticide-laden micromoths, documented by R. F. Reidinger, Jr., of the University of Arizona, provides grounds for concern for the future of a species considered too abundant ever to be in peril.

Noncave bats do not escape modern hazards unscathed. Bats which visit or occupy man-made structures are affected in direct relationship to the degree of man's use of pesticides. Current use of insecticides—particularly DDT in the widespread irrigated farmlands of Sonora and Sinaloa in Mexico and, until recently, in Arizona—is believed to be responsible for a staggering reduction in numbers of *Tadarida*. The guano bat is especially vulnerable because of its long-distance foraging flights and its northward migration through Mexico in early spring when heavy agricultural spraying is carried on.

There are several well-documented cases of major bat die-offs in northern Mexico and the southwestern United States. Dead and dying bats littered the landscape around the Cave of the Tiger near Carbo, Sonora, in 1968 and around Eagle Creek Cave in the same year. Specimens from the latter site were examined for rabies, but tests were negative. Tests for DDT, however, were positive.

Earlier experiments by M. M. Luckens and W. H. Davis had shown that bats in autumn were many times more tolerant of doses of DDT than were laboratory animals such as mice, rats, and rabbits. DDT—or its metabolized form, DDE—was stored in fatty tissues which were gradually oxidized during the winter. By spring the pesticide represented a hazardous residue, potentially fatal under the stress of migration or following the ingestion of additional amounts while feeding on insects that were poisoned but still able to fly. Since the banning of the use of most chlorinated chemicals (except under special dispensation from the Environmental Protection Agency), some relief for wildlife, including bats, has been achieved. But the legal use of many other chemicals still poses serious threats to the survival of nature's most effective biological controllers of certain species of harmful insects. And nursing females pass the poisons on to the young.

I am particularly concerned that efforts be made to try to devise substitute roost or hibernation sites when buildings are scheduled for "bat-proofing"—30,000 little brown bats were exterminated in the top floor of Old Main at Southern Illinois University, and thousands have been destroyed in attics of old homes and other structures—or when access to caves, mines, or tunnels is blocked.

Tunnels—for Bats or Cars? I tried to save thousands of bats in old railroad tunnel wintering sites when work on the Pennsylvania Turnpike tunnels began in 1938. Fifty years earlier man had created ideal wintering quarters—half-finished railroad tunnels. Bats accepted them. Now they were about to be evacuated. "They're just like caves," geologist Arthur Cleaves told me as he described the series of tunnels in nine ridges of the Allegheny Mountains in south central Pennsylvania. "There are bushels of bats—they're everywhere."

Rough access roads led to the entrances. Blue Mountain and Kittatinny Mountain are separated by a valley only a few hundred yards

Abandoned railroad tunnels in Pennsylvania provided cavelike hibernacula until they became turnpike tunnels.

across, but the facing cavelike tunnels were very different. Kittatinny Tunnel, to the west, appeared ready for almost immediate use as a vehicular tunnel—until we came to a dead end 2,400 feet inside. The temperature in mid-March was 46° F. inside, 28° F. outside. We found nearly 3,500 bats there, more than in any other Pennsylvania cave but one.

Not a single tunnel had been "holed through." Tunneling stopped in the 1880s when the enterprise went broke. Before our arrival this eastern portion of Kittatinny Tunnel had been drained of 3 to 4 feet of water, but the opposite, west end of Blue Mountain Tunnel was still flooded by a 15-foot dam formed by rockslides from the hillside above the portal. Exploration by canoe failed to turn up any bats on the low ceiling of the underground lake.

The other end of Blue Mountain Tunnel looked eastward over farmland in the distance and had the most exposed portal. Here temperature fluctuation evidently influenced the makeup of the bat population. Most of these were the hardy big brown bat, *Eptesicus,* but only 175 bats used this 1,890-foot tunnel. Bats were fewer and fewer in the next six tunnels as we moved west. The engineers had warned us that the more horizontal rock strata in the western ridges were less stable. Rockfalls were common, bats scarce.

Tunneling operations were well under way by the next autumn. Before the winter ended, the bats would be dislodged. Could we find other hibernating quarters for them? Would they accept new winter quarters? Since we could move them during their dormant period, there seemed to be a good chance that they might stay in caves until spring and come back to them in the fall. We decided to find out.

Fred Ulmer, my co-worker at the Academy of Natural Sciences of Philadelphia, joined me one weekend in December 1930 on a trip to the east tunnel in Kittatinny Mountain. There we gathered 150 bats, among them a dozen that I had banded the previous winter. Then we backtracked 25 miles to Conodoguinet Cave on the outskirts of Carlisle.

The bats were now wide awake as we started banding at the cave entrance. Most flew into the cave, but some circled once or twice and then headed west in a beeline for the tunnels.

Five weeks later we returned. Directly over the cave a highway crew was surveying for the future turnpike. Just inside the entrance we found Bat No. 1736. On the cave floor were ten banded bats, dead, trampled into the mud. In an obscure crevice we found two live ones, No. 1847 and No. 1848. A few more had been missed by marauding visitors. The transfer idea might work, but this cave obviously was too well known and offered too few hiding places. A more remote cave was needed. I had just the spot in mind—Aitkin Cave, 80 miles to the north, the state's leading bat cave.

We reached Kittatinny Tunnel in the nick of time. Operations were crowding the bats into a steadily diminishing space in the old tunnel. Fully 5,000 bats hung in scattered clusters, some within a few hundred feet of the workings, seemingly undisturbed by the terrific din set up by the drilling equipment and the exhaust fans. Helmeted tunnel workers stared as we swept hundreds of bats into containers.

Freezing rain soaked us on the quarter-mile trips between the car and Aitkin Cave with our equipment and cages. After two hours in the ice-filled cave entrance, attaching the tiny aluminum bands and recording the species and sex of each bat, we reluctantly decided to release several thousand still unbanded. At least we were giving them a chance for survival. We trudged back through the rain with our empty cages and set out for Philadelphia.

That spring and summer the turnpike was pushed to swift completion. Many times Fred Ulmer and I talked about the bats. A farmer found one of our banded pipistrelles 50 miles east of the tunnel where we banded it. Would the bats go back to Aitkin Cave? Or would they become victims of habit and seek their former haunts, the old tunnels, now vastly altered?

When winter had settled in, we began the search for the tunnel bats.

At Aitkin Cave mats of bats covered large sections of the smooth, arched walls, filling in the spaces between pincushions of stalactites and crowding bowllike pockets in the ceiling. But we couldn't find a single banded bat. They must be elsewhere, we thought, perhaps in the tunnels. The superhighway had been opened in October. It took only a minute to drive through Blue Mountain's well-lighted, concrete-lined, mile-long tunnel. Just beyond, we pulled off the road in front of the portal house at Kittatinny Tunnel.

"You fellows should have been here this fall," the operators said. "For six weeks there were bats flying in and out of the tunnels. Hundreds of them every night until cold weather set in."

What had become of them? The bats found no hibernating quarters in the airy, well-lighted, smooth-walled tunnels. Had they been able to find shelter in natural caves? We searched the few small caves nearby. In none was there more than a score of bats; none were banded. Where had they gone? Some may have found shelter in crevices too small for man to enter. For years I hoped that some sharp-eyed spelunker would find a few banded bats. No one ever did.

Unwanted Tenants. No matter how much a person may appreciate the wonders of bat performances and their contribution to a healthy ecosystem, the unpleasantness of sharing living quarters with them can become intolerable. Thousands of nursery roosts and an uncounted number of male aggregations of little brown bats and their varied kin exist in structures used by man. In towns and cities, however, more people doubtless are familiar with the big brown bat, *Eptesicus fuscus.* This larger bat thrives in attics and behind the trim below the roof of even recently built houses. How can bats be persuaded to move out? When their roosting places can be located, a liberal deposit of mothballs or naphthalene flakes will generally drive out the bats long enough for someone to find and seal off their points of access to the building. In summer, air conditioning or the use of electric fans may

When bright lights, bat repellents, and efforts to seal off access all fail, public health workers may be needed to drive bats from living quarters.

create an environment too cool or windy for a nursery colony. Their environment can also be altered by raising the level of illumination. In Canada, M. Brock Fenton found that many nursery groups left when floodlights were set up in attic roosts. The odor from accumulations of guano is so persistent, however, that bats will recognize it and repopulate the site if they can still get in. Glass-wool insulation stuffed into roosting spaces is often effective.

In 1974 environmentalists in New England organized Endangered Species Productions, Inc., a professional group experienced in the use of advertising and marketing techniques. ESP has been vigorously working to change the ugly image of bats that still persists. Enlisting the aid of bat experts and wildlife regulatory agencies as well as work-

137

ing with schools and news media, ESP seems to be making impressive headway toward its very worthwhile goal—helping threatened species of wildlife, from bats to whales, to continue to perform their natural roles in a healthier world ecosystem. Active, widespread support for ESP and other national, well-conceived conservation efforts can bring about a major improvement in man's treatment of long mistreated, misunderstood species of wildlife.

Bibliography

RECOMMENDED BOOKS

Allen, Glover M. 1939. Bats. Harvard University Press, Cambridge. 368 pp. (Reprint 1962, Dover Publications, New York)

Baer, George M. (ed.). 1975. The natural history of rabies. 2 vol. Academic Press, New York.

Banfield, A. W. F. 1974. The mammals of Canada. University of Toronto Press. 438 pp.

Barbour, Roger W., and Wayne H. Davis. 1969. Bats of America. University Press of Kentucky, Lexington. 286 pp.

————. 1974. Mammals of Kentucky. University Press of Kentucky, Lexington. 322 pp.

Burt, William H., and Richard P. Grossenheider. 1952. A field guide to the mammals. Houghton Mifflin Co., Boston. 200 pp.

Findley, J. S., A. H. Harris, D. E. Wilson, and C. Jones. 1975. Mammals of New Mexico. University of New Mexico Press, Albuquerque. 360 pp.

Griffin, Donald R. 1958. Listening in the dark: The acoustic orientation of bats and man. Yale University Press, New Haven. 413 pp.

————. 1959. Echoes of bats and men. Anchor Books, New York.

Hall, E. Raymond, and Keith R. Kelson. 1959. The mammals of North America, Vol. 1 (Bats of North & Middle America, pp. 79–217). The Ronald Press Co., New York. 546 pp.

Halliday, William R. 1974. American caves and caving. Harper & Row, New York. 348 pp.

Lauber, Patricia. 1968. Bats: Wings in the night. Random House, New York. 80 pp.

Lundelius, E. L., and B. H. Slaughter (eds.). 1971. Natural history of Texas caves. Gulf Natural History, Dallas. 174 pp.

Mohr, Charles E., and Thomas L. Poulson. 1966. The life of the cave. McGraw-Hill Book Co., New York. 232 pp.

————, and Howard N. Sloane. 1955. Celebrated American caves. Rutgers University Press, New Brunswick, N.J. 339 pp.

Novick, Alvin, and Nina Leen. 1969. The world of bats. Holt, Rinehart and Winston, New York. 171 pp.

Palmer, Ralph S. 1954. The mammal guide. Doubleday and Co., Garden City, New York. 384 pp.

Peterson, Russell. 1964. Silently, by night. McGraw-Hill Book Co., New York. 227 pp.

Ripper, Charles L. 1954. Bats. William Morrow & Co., New York. 64 pp.

Slaughter, Bob H., and Dan W. Walton (eds.). 1970. About bats: A chiropteran biology symposium. Southern Methodist University Press, Dallas. 339 pp.

Turner, Dennis C. 1975. The vampire bat: A field study in behavior and ecology. Johns Hopkins University Press, Baltimore. 145 pp.

Vaughan, Terry A. 1972. Mammalogy. W. B. Saunders Co., Philadelphia. 463 pp.

Wimsatt, William A. (ed.). 1970. Biology of bats. 2 vols. Academic Press, New York.

Zim, Herbert S., and Donald F. Hoffmeister. 1955. Mammals. Golden Press, New York. 160 pp.

SOURCES

Note: The items listed below were almost exclusively published between 1969 and 1975. For references prior to 1969 the reader should consult *Bats of America* by Roger W. Barbour and Wayne H. Davis.

Altenbach, J. S., and M. G. Petit. 1972. Stratification of guano deposits of the free-tailed bat, *Tadarida brasiliensis.* J. Mamm, 53:890–893.

Baker, J. K. 1961. What about bats? Carlsbad Caverns Nat. Hist. Assoc. 55 pp.

———. 1963. Fossilization of bat skeletons in the Carlsbad Caverns. Bull. Natl. Speleol. Soc., 25:37–44.

Black, H. L. 1972. Differential exploitation of moths by the bats *Eptesicus fuscus* and *Lasiurus cinereus.* J. Mamm., 53:598–601.

———. 1974. A north temperate bat community: Structure and prey populations. J. Mamm., 55:138–157.

Bogan, M. A. 1972. Observations on parturition and development in the hoary bat, *Lasiurus cinereus.* J. Mamm., 53:598–604.

Braaksma, S., and W. P. T. Van der Drift. 1972. Bats pesticides conflicts. TNO-news, 27:579–583.

Bradbury, J. W. 1968. Mechanisms of target discrimination by the echolocating bat, *Vampyrum spectrum.* Ph.D. dissertation, The Rockefeller University. 160 pp.

———. 1972. The silent symphony: Tuning in on the bat. Pp. 112–124 *in* The marvels of animal behavior. Natl. Geogr. Soc., Washington, D.C.

———, and F. Nettebohm. 1969. The use of vision by the little brown bat, *Myotis lucifugus,* under controlled conditions. Animal Behav., 17:480–485.

Brown, P. E. 1973. Vocal communication and the development of hearing in the pallid bat, *Antrozous pallidus.* Ph.D. dissertation, Univ. California, Los Angeles. 141 pp.

Buchler, E. R. 1975. Food transit time in *Myotis lucifugus* (Chiroptera: Vespertilionidae). J. Mamm., 56:252–255.

————. 1975. A chemiluminescent tag for tracking bats and other small nocturnal animals. J. Mamm. *In press.*

————. 1975. Prey selection by *Myotis lucifugus* (Chiroptera: Vespertilionidae). *In press.*

Chase, J. 1972. The role of vision in echolocating bats. Ph.D. dissertation, Indiana University, Bloomington. 214 pp.

Cockrum, E. L. 1969. Migration of the guano bat *Tadarida brasiliensis.* Pp. 303–336 *in* Contributions in mammalogy, J. K. Jones, Jr. (ed.). Univ. of Kansas, Mus. of Nat. History Misc. Publ. No. 51.

————. 1972. Bats and man. Defenders of Wildlife, Part I, July–Aug. 364–367; Part II, Sept.–Oct. 452–456. Rachel Carson Mem. Wildl. Educ. Fund Study, Nos. 18, 20.

————, and B. J. Hayward. 1968. Hummingbird bats. Natural History. 71(8):38–43.

Constantine, D. G. 1948. Great bat colonies attract predators. Bull. Natl. Speleol. Soc., 10:100.

————. 1967. Activity patterns of the Mexican free-tailed bat. Univ. New Mexico. Publ. Biol., No. 7. 79 pp.

————. 1970. Health, welfare, and economy. Pp. 319–424 *in* Biology of bats, Vol. 2, W. A. Wimsatt (ed.). Academic Press, New York.

————, R. W. Emmons, and J. D. Woodie. 1972. Rabies virus in nasal mucosa of naturally infected bats. Science, 1755:1255–1256.

Cope, J. B., and S. R. Humphrey. 1972. Reproduction of the bats *Myotis keenii* and *Pipistrellus subflavus* in Indiana. Bat Res. News, 13:9–10.

Coutts, R. A. 1972. The development of a technique to determine insect species from stomach contents and feces of some bats. M.S. dissertation, Carleton University, Ottawa, Canada. 53 pp.

————, M. B. Fenton, and E. Glenn. 1973. Food intake by captive *Myotis lucifugus* and *Eptesicus fuscus* (Chiroptera: Vespertilionidae). J. Mamm., 54:985–990.

Davis, R. 1969. Growth and development of young pallid bats, *Antrozous pallidus.* J. Mamm., 50:729–736.

Davis, W. H. 1964. Fall swarming of bats at Dixon Cave, Kentucky. Bull. Natl. Speleol. Soc., 26:82–83.

————. 1965. Bats dying in Missouri caves. Bat Res. News, 6:36.

Bibliography

————. 1967. Bats needed for research? Bat Res. News, 8:12.

————, and R. W. Barbour. 1970. Homing in blinded bats (*Myotis sodalis*). J. Mamm., 51:182–184.

————, and H. B. Hitchcock. 1965. Biology and migration of the bat, *Myotis lucifugus,* in New England. J. Mamm., 46:296–315.

Druecker, J. D. 1972. Aspects of reproduction in *Myotis volans, Lasionycteris noctivagans,* and *Lasiurus cinereus.* Ph.D. dissertation, University of New Mexico, Albuquerque. 70 pp.

Dunning, D. C., and K. D. Roeder. 1965. Moth sounds and insect-catching behavior of bats. Science. 147:173–174.

Easterla, D. A. 1973. Ecology of the 18 species of chiroptera at Big Bend National Park, Texas. Northwest Missouri State Univ. Studies 34:1–165.

————, and P. Easterla. 1969. America's rarest mammal. Natl. Wildlife, 7(5):14–18.

————. 1974. Rare glimpses of newborn bats. Smithsonian, 5(7):104–107.

Ellins, S. R., and F. A. Masterson. 1971. Brightness discrimination thresholds in the bat, *Eptesicus fuscus.* Bull. Ecol. Soc. Amer., 52(4):41–42.

Environmental Protection Agency. 1972. EPA order banning general use of DDT in the U.S.A. as of Dec. 31, 1972. Order and Opinion of Administrator. EPA, Washington, D.C.

Fenton, M. B. 1969. Ecological studies of bats in Ontario and adjacent regions. Ph.D. dissertation, University of Toronto.

————. 1969. The carrying of young by females of three species of bats. Canadian J. Zool., 47:158–159.

————. 1970. A technique for monitoring bat activity with results obtained from different environments in southern Ontario. Canadian J. Zool., 48:847–851.

————. 1970. Population studies of *Myotis lucifugus* (Chiroptera: Vespertilionidae) in Ontario. Life Sci. Contrib., Royal Ontario Mus., 77:1–34.

————. 1971. Bats . . . questions, answers & issues. Ontario Nat., 9:12–19.

————, and K. D. Roeder. 1974. The microtymbols of some Arctiidae.

Jour. Lepidopterists' Soc., 28(3):205–211.

————, S. L. Jacobson, and R. N. Stone. 1973. An automatic ultrasonic sensing system for monitoring the activity of some bats. Canadian J. Zool., 51:291–299.

Findley, J. S. 1973. The status of southwestern bat populations. Pp. 12–17 *in* Symposium on rare and endangered wildlife of the southwestern United States. New Mexico Dept. Game and Fish, Santa Fe. 167 pp.

————, E. H. Studier, and D. E. Wilson. 1972. Morphologic properties of bat wings. J. Mamm., 53:429–444.

Fleming, T. H., E. T. Hooper, and D. E. Wilson. 1972. Three Central American bat communities: structure, reproductive cycles, and movement patterns. Ecology, 53:555–569.

Gillette, D. D., and J. D. Kimbrough. 1970. Chiropteran mortality. Pp. 262–283 *in* About bats, B. Slaughter and D. Walton (eds.). Southern Methodist University Press, Dallas.

Goehring, H. H. 1972. Twenty-year study of *Eptesicus fuscus* in Minnesota. J. Mamm., 53:201–207.

Gould, Edwin. 1975. Neonatal vocalizations in bats of eight genera. J. Mamm., 56:15–29.

Greenhall, A. M. 1972. The problem of bat rabies, migratory bats, livestock and wildlife. Trans. 37th North American Wildlife and Natural Resources Conference, 12–15 March. Washington, D.C., Wildlife Management Institute.

————. 1972. The biting and feeding habits of the vampire bat, *Desmodus rotundus*. J. Zool., 168:451–461.

————. 1973. Indiana bat: A cave-dweller in trouble. Natl. Parks & Cons. Mag., 47(8):14–17.

————. 1973. Status and proposed recovery plan—the Indiana bat, *Myotis sodalis*. Bird and Mammal Laboratories, U.S. Bur. Sport Fisheries & Wildl.

————. 1974. Vampire bat control. Bull. Pan. Am. Health Org., 8(1):30–36.

————, and J. L. Paradiso. 1968. Bats and bat banding. U.S. Bur. Sport Fisheries and Wildl. Res. Publ. 72 pp.

Bibliography

Griffin, D. R. 1940. Migrations of New England bats. Bull. Mus. Comp. Zool., 86:217–246.

————. 1946. Mystery mammals of the twilight. Natl. Geogr. Mag., 7:117–134.

————. 1953. Deluge underground. Bull. Natl. Speleol. Soc., 15:34–37.

————. 1969. Bats—animal sonar experts. Pp. 12–16 *in* The world of darkness. Animal Kingdom, Special Issue, N.Y. Zool. Soc. 72(3).

————. 1970. Migrations and homing of bats. Pp. 233–263 *in* Biology of bats, Vol. 2, W. A. Wimsatt (ed.). Academic Press, New York.

————. 1971. The importance of atmospheric attenuation for the echolocation of bats (Chiroptera). Animal Behav., 19:55–61.

Grout, C. M., and T. C. Williams. 1973. Observations of bats 1,000 meters below ground level. Bat Res. News, 14:26–27.

Guilday, J. E., and H. W. Hamilton. 1973. The late Pleistocene small mammals of Eagle Cave, Pendleton County, West Virginia. Carnegie Mus. Annals, 44:45–58.

Gunier, W. J. 1971. Stress-induced abortion in bats. Bat Res. News, 12:4.

————, and W. H. Elder. 1971. Experimental homing of gray bats to a maternity colony in a Missouri barn. Amer. Midland Nat., 86:502–506.

Gut, H. J. 1959. A pleistocene vampire bat from Florida. J. Mamm., 40:534–538.

Hall, J. S. 1962. A life history and taxonomic study of the Indiana bat, *Myotis sodalis*. Reading [Pa.] Public Museum and Art Gallery Sci. Publ., 12:1–68.

————. 1964. Bat hibernation in the Mammoth Cave region of Kentucky. Bull. Natl. Speleol. Soc., 26:71–72.

————, and F. J. Brenner. 1968. Summer netting of bats at a cave in Pennsylvania. J. Mamm., 49:779–791.

Hardin, J. W., and M. D. Hassell. 1970. Observation of waking periods and movements of *Myotis sodalis* during hibernation. J. Mamm., 51:829–831.

Harris, J. A. 1970. Bat-guano cave environment. Science, 169:1342–1343.

Hassell, M. D. 1967. Intra-cave activity of four species of bats hibernating in Kentucky. Ph.D. dissertation, University of Kentucky.

Hawkey, C. 1966. A plasminogen activator in the saliva of the vampire bat *Desmodus rotundus*. J. Physiol., 183:55–56.

Hayward, B. J. 1970. The natural history of the cave bat *Myotis velifer.* WRI-SCI (Western New Mexico Univ.), 1:1–74.

———, and E. L. Cockrum. 1971. The natural history of the western long-nosed bat, *Leptonycteris sanborni*. WRI-SCI (Western New Mexico Univ.), 1:75–123.

Heatherington, M. T. 1971. Thermal response of the little brown bat (*Myotis lucifugus lucifugus*) to drugs acting on the sympathetic nervous system. Ph.D. dissertation, Purdue University. 203 pp.

Henshaw, R. E. 1972. Niche specificity and adaptability in cave bats. Bull. Natl. Speleol. Soc., 34:61–70.

Hitchcock, H. B. 1965. Twenty-three years of bat banding in Ontario and Quebec. Canadian Field-Nat., 79:4–14.

———. 1974. Reflections of a batman. Massachusetts Wildl., 25(1): 8–13.

Hoffmeister, D. V. 1970. The seasonal distribution of bats in Arizona: A case for improving mammalian range maps. Southwestern Nat., 15:11–22.

Holt, E. J. 1969. Physiological response of the bat *Eptesicus fuscus* to thermal stress. Ph.D. dissertation, Purdue University. 207 pp.

Hooper, J. H. D. 1964. Bats and the amateur naturalist. Studies in Speleol., 1(1):9–15.

Horst, R. 1972. Bats as primary producers in an ecosystem. Bull. Natl. Speleol. Soc., 34:49–54.

Howell, D. J. 1972. Physiological adaptations in the syndrome of chiropterophily with emphasis on the bat *Leptonycteris* Lydekker. Ph.D. dissertation, University of Arizona. 262 pp.

———. 1972. Adaptive morphology of the tongue of nectar-feeding bats. Bat Res. News, 13(4):64.

Humphrey, S. R. 1969. Disturbances and bats. Oklahoma Underground, 2:42–44.

———. 1971. Population ecology of the little brown bat, *Myotis lucifugus,* in Indiana and north-central Kentucky. Ph.D. dissertation,

Oklahoma State University. 138 pp.

―――. 1971. Photographic estimation of population size of the Mexican free-tailed bat, *Tadarida brasiliensis*. Amer. Midland Nat., 86:220–223.

―――. 1972. Adaptations of refuging free-tailed bats. Bat Res. News, 13(2):19–26.

―――. 1973. Topic for discussion: Bats and human disease. Bat Res. News, 14:52–54.

―――, and J. B. Cope. 1970. Population samples of the evening bat, *Nycticeius humeralis*. J. Mamm., 51:399–401.

―――. 1975. Population ecology of the little brown bat (*Myotis lucifugus*) in Indiana and north-central Kentucky. Spec. Publ., Amer. Soc. Mamm., *in press*.

Hutchison, J. H. 1967. A Pleistocene vampire bat (*Desmodus stocki*) from Potter Creek cave, Shasta County, California. Paleobios (Berkeley), 3:1–6.

Jeffries, D. J. 1972. Organochlorine insecticide residues in British bats and their significance. J. Zool., 166(2):245–263.

Jepsen, G. L. 1970. Bat origins and evolution. Pp. 1–64 *in* Biology of bats, Vol. 1, W. A. Wimsatt (ed.). Academic Press, New York.

Jones, C., and R. D. Suttkus. 1973. Notes on netting bats for eleven years in western New Mexico. Southwestern Nat., 16:261–266.

Kaplan, M. M., and H. Koprowski (eds.). 1973. Laboratory techniques in rabies. World Health Org., Geneva. Monograph Series No. 23, third edition. 367 pp. (United Nations, New York)

Kennedy, M. L., and T. L. Best. 1972. Flight speed of the gray bat, *Myotis grisescens*. Amer. Midland Nat., 88:254–255.

Koopman, K. F., and J. K. Jones, Jr. 1970. Classification of bats. Pp. 22–28 *in* About bats, B. H. Slaughter and D. W. Walton (eds.). Southern Methodist University Press, Dallas.

Kunz, T. H. 1971. Ecology of the cave bat, *Myotis velifer*, in south-central Kansas and northwestern Oklahoma. Ph.D. dissertation, Univ. Kansas. 148 pp.

―――. 1973. Resource utilization: Temporal and spatial components of bat activity in central Iowa. J. Mamm., 54:14–32.

―――. 1973. Population studies of the cave bat (*Myotis velifer*): Reproduction, growth, and development. Occas. Papers Mus. Nat. Hist., Univ. Kansas, 15:1–43.

————. 1974. Feeding ecology of a temperate insectivorous bat (*Myotis velifer*). Ecology, 55:693–711.

————, and M. B. Fenton. 1973. Resource partitioning by *Eptesicus fuscus* and *Lasiurus cinereus*. Bat Res. News, 14:55–56.

Lee, D. S., and M. D. Tuttle. 1970. Old Indian Cave: Florida's first bat sanctuary. Florida Nat., 43:150–152.

Linhart, S. B. 1975. Age determination and occurrence of incremental growth lines in the dental cementum of the common vampire bat (*Desmodus rotundus*). J. Mamm., 54:493–496.

Lowman, G. E. 1975. A survey of endangered, threatened, rare, status undetermined, peripheral, and unique mammals of the southeastern national forests and grasslands. U.S. Dept. Agr., Forest Service. 32 pp.

Luckens, M. M., and W. H. Davis. 1964. Toxicity of dieldrin and endrin to bats. Nature, 207:879–880.

————, J. VanEps, and W. H. Davis. 1971. Transit time through the digestive tract of the bat, *Eptesicus fuscus*. Exp. Med. Surg., 29:25–28.

McCue, J. J. G., Jr. 1961. How bats hunt with sound. Natl. Geogr. Mag. 119:570–578.

McKinley, E. G. 1971. Environmental aspects concerning the onset of the foraging flight of the cave bat *Myotis velifer*. Ph.D. dissertation, University of Arizona. 126 pp.

McManus, J. J. 1974. Activity and thermal preference of the little brown bat, *Myotis lucifugus,* during hibernation. J. Mamm., 55:844–846.

————, and R. J. Esher. 1971. Notes on the biology of the little brown bat, *Myotis lucifugus,* hibernating in New Jersey. New Jersey Acad. Sci., 16(1–2):19–24.

McNab, B. K. 1971. The structure of tropical bat faunas. Ecology, 52:352–358.

————. 1973. Energetics and the distribution of vampires. J. Mamm. 54:131–144.

————. 1974. The behavior of temperate cave bats in a subtropical environment. Ecology, 55:943–958.

Mills, R. S. 1971. A concentration of *Myotis keenii* at caves in Ohio, J. Mamm., 52:625.

Mitchell, G. C. 1969. An electrophoretic comparison of hemoglobins in the bat family Vespertilionidae. Ph.D. dissertation, University of Arizona. 76 pp.

————, and R. J. Burns. 1973. Chemical control of vampire bats. Denver: U.S. Bureau of Sport Fisheries and Wildlife. 36 pp.

————, and J. R. Tigner. 1970. The route of ingested blood in the vampire bat (*Desmodus rotundus*). J. Mamm., 51:814–817.

Mitchell, R. W., and J. R. Reddell. 1971. The invertebrate fauna of Texas caves. Pp. 35–90 *in* Natural history of Texas caves, E. L. Lundelius and B. H. Slaughter (eds.). Gulf Natural History, Dallas.

Mogus, M. A. E. 1970. A theoretical approach to bat echolocation. Ph.D. dissertation, Pennsylvania State University. 116 pp.

Mohl, N. D. 1971. Craniofacial relationships and adaptations in bats. Ph.D. dissertation, State University of New York—Buffalo. 350 pp.

Mohr, C. E. 1942. Bat tagging in Pennsylvania turnpike tunnels. J. Mamm., 23:375–379.

————. 1948. Texas bat caves served in three wars. Bull. Natl. Speleol. Soc., 10:89–96.

————. 1952. Audubon's bats. Audubon Mag., 54(3):172–179.

————. 1953. Possible causes of an apparent decline in wintering populations of cave bats. NSS News, 11:4–5.

————. 1964. Exploring America underground. Natl. Geogr. Mag., 125(6):803–837.

————. 1968. Bats. Explorers Journ., 46:172–179.

————. 1970. Underground adventure. Pp. 222–231 *in* Vacationland U.S.A. Natl. Geogr. Soc., Washington, D.C.

————. 1972. Delaware issues a bat alert. Delaware Conservationist, 16(3):22–23.

————. 1972. The status of threatened species of cave-dwelling bats. Bull. Natl. Speleol. Soc., 34(2):33–47.

Myers, R. F. 1964. Ecology of three species of myotine bats in the

Ozark Plateau. Ph.D. dissertation, University of Missouri. 210 pp.

Novick, A. 1971. Echolocation in bats: Some aspects of pulse design. Amer. Sci., 59(2):198–209.

————. 1973. Bats aren't all bad. Natl. Geogr. Mag., 143:614–637.

————, and B. A. Dale. 1971. Foraging behavior in fishing bats and their insectivorous relatives. J. Mamm., 52:817–818.

O'Farrell, M. J., and W. G. Bradley. 1970. Activity patterns of bats over a desert spring. J. Mamm., 51:18–26.

————, and B. W. Miller. 1972. Pipistrelle bats attracted to vocalizing females and to a blacklight insect trap. Amer. Midland Nat., 88:462–463.

————, and E. H. Studier. 1973. Reproduction, growth, and development in *Myotis thysanodes* and *M. lucifugus* (Chiroptera: Vespertilionidae). Ecology, 54:18–30.

Office of Endangered Species and International Activities. 1973. Threatened wildlife of the United States. Government Printing Office, Washington, D.C. 289 pp.

————. 1974. United States list of endangered fauna. Fish and Wildlife Service, Washington, D.C. 22 pp.

Orr, R. T. 1970. Development: Prenatal and postnatal. Pp. 217–231 *in* Biology of bats, Vol. 2, W. A. Wimsett (ed.). Academic Press, New York.

Packard, R. L., and T. R. Mollhagen. 1971. Bats of Texas. Pp. 122–132 *in* Natural history of Texas caves. E. L. Lundelius and B. H. Slaughter (eds.). Gulf Natural History, Dallas.

Pagels, J. F. 1970. The dynamics of temperature responses of the free-tailed bat, *Tadarida brasiliensis cynocephala* (LeConte). Ph.D. dissertation, Tulane University. 155 pp.

Perry, M. L. 1947. Chiquito—A guano bat. Natural History, 56(4):178–183.

Petit, M. G., and J. S. Altenbach. 1973. A chronological record of environmental chemicals from analysis of stratified vertebrate excretion deposited in a sheltered environment. Envir. Research, 6:339–343.

Bibliography

Pine, R. H. 1972. The bats of the genus *Carollia*. Texas Agri. Exper. Sta. Tech. Monographs, 8:1–225.

Pollack, G., O. W. Henson, Jr., and A. Novick. 1972. Cochlear potentials from flying bats. Physiol., 15:239.

Poole, E. L. 1932. A survey of the mammals of Berks County, Pennsylvania. Reading [Pa.] Public Mus. and Art Gallery Bull., No. 13. 74 pp.

Poulson, T. L. 1972. Bat guano ecosystems. Bull. Natl. Speleol. Soc., 34(2):55–59.

———, and W. B. White. 1969. The cave environment. Science, 165:971–981.

Racey, P. A. 1970. The breeding, care, and management of Vespertilionid bats in the laboratory. Lab. Anim., 4:171–183.

———, and R. E. Stebbings. 1972. Bats in Britain—A status report. Oryx, 11:319–327.

Reidinger, R. F., Jr. 1972. Factors influencing Arizona bat population levels. Ph.D. dissertation, Arizona State University. 172 pp.

Roberts, L. H. 1975. Confirmation of the echolocation pulse production mechanism of *Rousettus*. J. Mamm., 56:218–220.

Roeder, K. D., and M. B. Fenton. 1973. Acoustic responsiveness of *Scoliopteryx libatrix* L. (Lepidoptera: Noctuidae), a moth that shares hibernacula with some insectivorous bats. Canadian J. Zool., 51:681–685.

Ross, A. 1967. Ecological aspects of the food habits of insectivorous bats. Proc. West. Found. Vert. Zool., 1(4):201–263.

Roth, C. E. 1971. Flutters in the dark. Curious Naturalist, 11(2):2–15.

Simmons, J. A. 1968. The sonar sight of bats. Psychology Today, 2:50–57.

———. 1970. Depth perception by sonar in the bat *Eptesicus fuscus*. Ph.D. dissertation, Princeton University. 218 pp.

———. 1971. Echolocation in bats: signal processing in echoes for target range. Science, 171:925–928.

———, Howell, D. J., and Suga, N. 1975. Information content of bat sonar echoes. Amer. Sci., 63:204.

Smith, C. W. 1971. Rabies and the caver. NSS News, 29(5):60–63.

Snow, C. 1973. Habitat management series for endangered species/ Report No. 4. Spotted bat, *Euderma maculatum*. U.S. Bur. Land Manag. Tech. Note. 13 pp.

Stager, K. E. 1948. Falcons prey on Ney Cave bats. Bull. Natl. Speleol. Soc., 10:97–99.

Stebbings, R. E. 1970. Bats in danger. Oryx, 10(5):311–312.

Studier, E. H., and D. J. Howell. 1969. Heart rate of female big brown bats in flight. J. Mamm., 50:842–845.

———, and M. J. O'Farrell. 1972. Biology of *Myotis thysanodes* and *M. lucifugus* (Chiroptera: Vespertilionidae)—I. Thermoregulation. Comp. Biochem. Physiol., 41A:567–595.

Sulkin, S. E., and R. Allen. 1971. Potential hazards to investigations of bat inhabited caves. Pp. 149–154 *in* The Natural History of Texas Caves, E. L. Lundelius and B. H. Slaughter (eds.). Gulf Natural History, Dallas.

Suthers, R. A. 1970. Vision, olfaction, taste. Pp. 265–309 *in* Biology of bats, Vol. 2, W. A. Wimsatt (ed.). Academic Press, New York.

———, and J. M. Fattee. 1973. Fishing behavior and acoustic orientation by the bat (*Noctilio labialis*). Animal Behav., 21:61–66.

Thompson, R. D., G. C. Mitchell, and R. J. Burns, 1972. Vampire bat control by systemic treatment of livestock with an anticoagulant. Science, 177:806–807.

Treat, A. E. 1958. A case of peculiar parasitism. Natural History, 67:366–373.

Tucker, R. K., and D. G. Crabtree. 1970. Handbook of toxicity of pesticides to wildlife. U.S. Bur. Sport Fisheries and Wildl. Resour., Publ. 84. 131 pp.

Tuttle, M. D. 1974. Population ecology of the gray bat (*Myotis grisescens*). Ph.D. dissertation, University of Kansas. 109 pp.

———. 1974. An improved trap for bats. J. Mamm., 55:475–477.

———. 1974. Bat trapping: results and suggestions. Bat Res. News, 15(1):4–7.

———. 1975. Population ecology of the gray bat (*Myotis grisescens*): Factors influencing early growth and development. Occ. Papers, Mus. of Nat. Hist., Univ. of Kansas, 36:1–24.

Bibliography

Twente, J. W. 1954. Habitat selection of cavern-dwelling bats as illustrated by four vespertilionids, Ph.D. dissertation, University of Michigan.

VanDeusen, H. M., and R. F. Peterson. 1958. Chiroptera of New Guinea. Natural History, 67:452–459.

Vaughan, T. A. 1970. Adaptations for flight in bats. Pp. 127–143 *in* About bats, P. H. Slaughter and D. W. Walton (eds.). Southern Methodist University Press, Dallas.

Watkins, L. C. 1972. A technique for monitoring the nocturnal activity of bats, with comments on the activity patterns of the evening bat, *Nycticeius humeralis*. Trans. Kansas Acad. Sci., 74(3–4):261–268.

Whitaker, J. O., Jr., and R. E. Mumford. 1971. Notes on a collection of bats taken by mist-netting at an Indiana Cave. Amer. Midland Nat., 85:277–279.

————. 1971. Notes on occurrence and reproduction of bats in Indiana. Indiana Acad. Sci. Proc., 81:376–383.

Williams, T. C. 1968. Nocturnal orientation techniques of a neotropical bat. Ph.D. dissertation, The Rockefeller University. 174 pp.

————, L. C. Ireland, and J. M. Williams. 1973. High altitude flights of the free-tailed bat, *Tadarida brasiliensis*, observed with radar. J. Mamm., 54:807–821.

————, and J. M. Williams. 1970. Radio tracking of homing and feeding flights of a neotropical bat *Phyllostomus hastatus*. Animal Behav., 18:302–309.

Wilson, D. E., and J. S. Findley. 1972. Randomness in bat homing. Amer. Nat., 106:418–424.

Wimsatt, W. A. 1969. Transient behavior, nocturnal activity patterns, and feeding efficiency of vampire bats (*Desmodus rotundus*) under natural conditions. J. Mamm., 50:233–244.

Winkelman, J. R. 1971. Adaptations for nectar-feeding in Glossophagine bats. Ph.D. dissertation, University of Michigan, 129 pp.

Winkler, W. G., and D. B. Adams. 1972. Utilization of southwestern bat caves by terrestrial carnivores. Amer. Midland Nat., 8(1):191–200.

Young, A. M. 1971. Foraging of vampire bats (*Desmodus rotundus*) in

Atlantic wet lowland Costa Rica. Rev. Biol. Trop., 18(12):73–88.

Zervanos, S. M., and R. E. Henshaw. 1970. Graded effect of acclimatation temperature on thermagenesis in winter-captured little brown bats. Proc. Penna. Acad. Sci., 44:207–211.

Index

Italic page numbers indicate illustrations.

Index

Index

Index

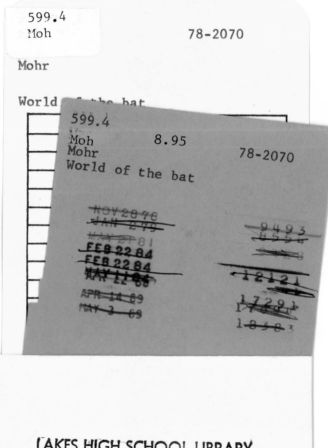